A Very Short Introduction to Everything

VERY SHORT INTRODUCTIONS are for anyone wanting a stimulating and accessible way in to a new subject. They are written by experts, and have been published in more than 25 languages worldwide.

The series began in 1995, and now represents a wide variety of topics in history, philosophy, religion, science, and the humanities. Over the next few years it will grow to a library of around 200 volumes – a Very Short Introduction to everything from ancient Egypt and Indian philosophy to conceptual art and cosmology.

Very Short Introductions available now:

Available soon:

AFRICAN HISTORY
  John Parker and Richard Rathbone
ANCIENT EGYPT   Ian Shaw
ART HISTORY   Dana Arnold
THE BRAIN   Michael O'Shea
BUDDHIST ETHICS
  Damien Keown
CAPITALISM   James Fulcher
CHAOS   Leonard Smith
CHRISTIAN ART   Beth Williamson
CHRISTIANITY   Linda Woodhead
CITIZENSHIP   Richard Bellamy
CLASSICAL ARCHITECTURE
  Robert Tavernor
CLONING   Arlene Judith Klotzko
CONTEMPORARY ART
  Julian Stallabrass
THE CRUSADES
  Christopher Tyerman
DADA AND SURREALISM
  David Hopkins
DERRIDA   Simon Glendinning
DESIGN   John Heskett
DINOSAURS   David Norman
DREAMING   J. Allan Hobson
ECONOMICS   Partha Dasgupta
EGYPTIAN MYTHOLOGY
  Geraldine Pinch
THE ELEMENTS   Philip Ball
THE END OF THE WORLD
  Bill McGuire
EXISTENTIALISM   Thomas Flynn
THE FIRST WORLD WAR
  Michael Howard

FREE WILL   Thomas Pink
FUNDAMENTALISM
  Malise Ruthven
HABERMAS   Gordon Finlayson
HIEROGLYPHS
  Penelope Wilson
HIROSHIMA   B. R. Tomlinson
HUMAN EVOLUTION
  Bernard Wood
INTERNATIONAL RELATIONS
  Paul Wilkinson
JAZZ   Brian Morton
MANDELA   Tom Lodge
MEDICAL ETHICS   Tony Hope
THE MIND   Martin Davies
MOLECULES   Philip Ball
MYTH   Robert Segal
NATIONALISM   Steven Grosby
PERCEPTION   Richard Gregory
PHILOSOPHY OF RELIGION
  Jack Copeland and
  Diane Proudfoot
PHOTOGRAPHY   Steve Edwards
THE PRESOCRATICS
  Catherine Osborne
THE RAJ   Denis Judd
THE RENAISSANCE
  Jerry Brotton
RENAISSANCE ART
  Geraldine Johnson
SARTRE   Christina Howells
THE SPANISH CIVIL WAR
  Helen Graham
TRAGEDY   Adrian Poole

For more information visit our web site

www.oup.co.uk/vsi

EVERYTHING

A Very Short Introduction

OXFORD
UNIVERSITY PRESS

OXFORD
UNIVERSITY PRESS

Great Clarendon Street, Oxford OX2 6DP

Oxford University Press is a department of the University of Oxford.
It furthers the University's objective of excellence in research, scholarship,
and education by publishing worldwide in

Oxford New York

Auckland Bangkok Buenos Aires Cape Town Chennai
Dar es Salaam Delhi Hong Kong Istanbul Karachi Kolkata
Kuala Lumpur Madrid Melbourne Mexico City Mumbai Nairobi
São Paulo Shanghai Taipei Tokyo Toronto

Oxford is a registered trade mark of Oxford University Press
in the UK and in certain other countries

Published in the United States
by Oxford University Press Inc., New York

First published as a Very Short Introduction 2003

British Library Cataloguing in Publication Data

Data available

Library of Congress Cataloging in Publication Data

Data available

ISBN 0-19-950294-3

1 3 5 7 9 10 8 6 4 2

Typeset by RefineCatch Ltd, Bungay, Suffolk
Printed in Great Britain by Clays Ltd., St. Ives plc

Contents

List of illustrations

The publisher and the author apologize for any errors or omissions in the above list. If contacted they will be pleased to rectify these at the earliest opportunity.

Very Short Introductions:
A Very Short History

'A thoroughly good idea. Snappy, small-format . . . stylish design . . .
perfect to pop in your pocket for spare moments'

Lisa Jardine

The *Very Short Introductions* series is phenomenally successful,
enjoying widespread critical acclaim. Perfect for train journeys,
holidays, and as a quick catch-up for busy people who want something
intellectually stimulating, the carefully selected authors combine
authoritative analysis, new ideas, and enthusiasm to provide much
more than a straightforward introduction to each topic.

These vibrant and accessible books can change the way you think about
the things that interest you, and are the perfect introduction to subjects
you previously knew nothing about. From a lucid explanation of the
essential issues in *Islam* to a lively insight into the complex theory of
Poststructuralism, and a non-technical assessment of the very matter
that makes up the universe in *Cosmology*, *Very Short Introductions*
make often challenging topics highly readable and have proven to be
extremely popular with general readers, as well as undergraduate
students and their lecturers.

The series was originally launched in 1995 with the first title, *Classics: A
Very Short Introduction*, and has quickly grown to become *the*
general introduction series for the intelligent reader worldwide, being

translated into over 25 languages. It will expand into a library of around 250 titles covering a wide range of key topics, from *The Brain* to *Ancient Egypt*, *Music* to *International Relations*, in subject areas such as history, philosophy, science, religion, politics, and the arts.

2003 sees the publication of the 100th title in the series, *Evolution: A Very Short Introduction*. This collection—*Everything, A Very Short Introduction*—has been put together to give you a taste of the series, with new articles by ten of the authors on their subject area, as well as snapshots of each title.

Chapter 1

How on earth
did we get here?

Introduction   **Philip Ball**

In 1638 two men met in a villa in Arcetri, near Florence. One was
a precocious 30-year-old Englishman, the other an ageing and
grey-bearded Italian natural philosopher. Under house arrest by
order of the Roman Catholic Church, Galileo was used to receiving
visitors curious about his astronomical theory, and his young guest
may have left little impression. But John Milton did not forget the
meeting.

When 20 years later Milton began his most famous work, the epic
poem *Paradise Lost*, the memory of Galileo must have haunted him.
He had been appalled by the unjust treatment meted out to the sage
of Pisa, and in his passionate defence of the freedom of speech,
Areopagitica (1644), he had described how Galileo's imprisonment
by the Inquisition 'for thinking in Astronomy otherwise than the
Franciscan and Dominican licensers thought' had 'damped the
glory of Italian wits'. Yet what is the universe of *Paradise Lost* but
the conventional hierarchical cosmos of Ptolemy, endorsed by
Christian theologians, with the heavens above and hell below a
static earth?

Samuel Johnson criticized *Paradise Lost* for its 'harsh and
barbarous' prose, but it is hard today not to feel more critical of
Milton's decision to ignore Galileo's science. Perhaps he felt
justified in taking poetic licence, retaining a stage design that fitted
the narrative. But Galileo's universe, with the sun at its centre and

3

the earth a mere planet in motion, probably left him deeply discomforted too. Certainly that seems to have been John Donne's feeling in 1611:

> And new Philosophy calls all in doubt,
> The Element of fire is quite put out;
> The Sun is lost, and th'earth, and no mans wit
> Can well direct him where to looke for it.

Today we find it intriguing and noteworthy when writers, poets, and artists look for inspiration and metaphor in science. In the 17th century that was a perfectly normal and deeply serious enterprise: John Donne, for all his misgivings, travelled to remote Linz in Austria to visit Johannes Kepler.

Clearly, artists did not always like what they found; but that did not exempt them from the obligation to be appraised of the metaphysical implications of new scientific discoveries. Milton's dilemma exemplifies the tensions between (to put it in stereotypical terms) the personal world-view of the artist and the objective perspective of the scientist; for Milton realized, even if he could not bring himself to articulate it, that things are not always as they seem, or as people believe them to be – or, indeed, as we would like them to be.

In cosmological terms that lesson is still being learned, while things have gone on getting ever stranger. Even Albert Einstein found himself misled by preconceptions when, in 1917, he fudged his equations describing a mathematical model of the universe to make it static and unchanging, as he thought it should be. When, 12 years later, Edwin Hubble discovered that the universe is expanding, Einstein admitted his 'blunder' – if he'd not been blinkered by expectations, he'd have been able to predict Hubble's finding.

That discovery, meanwhile, revised Galileo (and his predecessor Nicolaus Copernicus) once again. Astronomers had long since

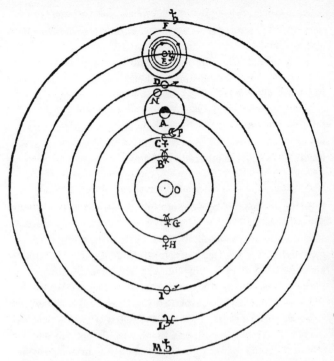

1. Galileo's presentation of the Copernican universe in his *Dialogue*. Unlike in Copernicus' representation, the earth is not alone in carrying a satellite.

displaced the sun from the centre of the universe: it is merely the centre of our solar system, on the fringes of our galaxy, in an undistinguished corner of an immeasurably vast cosmos. But now this universe had a beginning. Play the Hubble expansion backwards and all converges to a point: the eye of the Big Bang, as maverick astronomer Fred Hoyle dismissively named this moment of creation.

For astronomy, the post-Copernican era has been a voyage into both revelation and ignorance. We know our place now; but the cosmos is as mysterious as ever, arguably even more so. We know (or think we know) that most of the mass in the universe is invisible to us, and of unknown and exotic nature. Thanks to observations made over just the past five years or so, we know (or think we know) that the universe is not just expanding but accelerating, seeming to imply that all of space is filled with some 'vacuum energy' that counteracts gravity and pushes everything apart. One interpretation is that Einstein was right after all to add a fudge factor (called the cosmological constant) to his equations – it was no blunder. We know, in other words, not to be too certain about anything.

Even the understanding of our own planet has been revised almost beyond recognition in the past 100 years. The ground on which we stand, the archetype of solidity, has become a constantly shifting mosaic thanks to the theory of continental drift introduced (to much derision, if not exactly Galilean persecution) by Alfred Wegener in the 1930s. The continental plates are merely a veneer, riding on a mantle of hot, extremely viscous rock that churns in great overturning rolls in the earth's bowels, rearranging the face of the planet over millions of years. In other words, not only our cosmic maps but even our world maps are but snapshots, destined one day for redundancy.

By the same token, we are forced to accept the contingency of our climate, our seas, our atmosphere. The ice ages, first identified by Swiss geologist Louis Agassiz in the 1830s, forced scientists to take a dynamic view of the natural environment, culminating in the 'astronomical theory' of climate change proposed by Serbian mathematician Milutin Milankovitch in the 1920s. Periodic changes in the shape of the earth's orbit around the sun lead to 'Milankovitch cycles' which, as they phase in and out of step with one another, create a complex but predictable change in the temperatures of the earth's surface. Climate science has been one of the most revolutionary of the earth sciences over the past two decades, revealing natural processes that, riding on the back of the orbital variations, can transform the global climate in a matter of decades, melting the ice caps entirely or plunging the globe into cold storage.

Cosmology   **Peter Coles**

The ideal starting point for anyone curious about the universe and how it began, this book covers both the history of cosmology and the latest developments in the field.

What is it?

Cosmology is everything that exists. The entire system of things that is the Universe encompasses the very large and the very small – the astronomical scale of stars and galaxies and the microscopic world of elementary particles. The aim of cosmology is to place all known physical phenomena within a single coherent framework. This is an ambitious goal, and significant gaps in our knowledge still remain. Nevertheless, there has been such rapid progress that many cosmologists regard this as something of a 'Golden Age'. An emerging consensus about the form and distribution of matter and energy in the Universe suggests that a complete understanding of it all may be within reach. But if history tells us anything, it is that we should expect surprises!

'Buy and read this book even if you never thought you were interested in cosmology. It is a masterpiece of lucidity.'

New Humanist

The History of Astronomy   **Michael Hoskin**

Astronomy's long history

Historians of astronomy work mainly with the surviving documents from the past, and with artefacts such as instruments and observatory buildings. But can we discover something of the role the sky played in the 'cosmovision' of those who lived in Europe and the Middle East *before* the invention of writing? Could there even have been a prehistoric science of astronomy, perhaps one that enabled an elite to predict eclipses?

Stonehenge, for example, faces midsummer sunrise in one direction and midwinter sunset in the other. How can we be sure that an alignment that to us is of astronomical significance was chosen by Stonehenge's architects for this very reason? Did it have some quite different motivation, or even occur purely by chance? To take another example, a monument built around 3000 BC that faces east may have been oriented on the rising of the Pleiades, a bright cluster of stars in the constellation Taurus. It may have faced midway between midsummer and midwinter sunrise. Perhaps there was a sacred mountain in that direction. Or the orientation may have been chosen simply to take advantage of the slope of the ground. How can we decide which of these, if any, was in the minds of the builders?

The Earth   **Martin Redfern**

How can you put a big round planet in a small flat book?

It is not an easy fit, but there could be two broadly different ways of attempting it. One is the bottom-up approach of geology: essentially, looking at the rocks. For centuries, geologists have scurried around on the surface of our planet with their little hammers, examining the different rock types and the mineral grains which make them up. With eye and microscope, electron probe and mass spectrometer, they have reduced the planet to its component parts. Then they have mapped out how the different rock types relate to one another and, through theory, observation, and experiment, they have worked out how they might have got there. It has been a huge undertaking and one that has brought

2. Planet earth, as seen from space.

deep insights. Collectively, the efforts of all those geologists have built a giant edifice on which future earth scientists can stand. But this introduction is not a guide to rocks and minerals and geological map-making. It is a portrait of a planet.

The new view on our old planet is the top-down approach of what has come to be known as earth systems science. It looks at the earth as a whole, and not just frozen in time in the moment we call now. Taken over the deep time of geology we begin to see our planet as a dynamic system, a series of processes and cycles. We can begin to understand what makes it tick.

Advice for the future

We are no longer the victims of our planet, we are the custodians of it. Through our inconsiderate greed for land and our disregard for pollution, we bite the hand that feeds us. But we do so at our own peril. We still have all our eggs in one basket, all our people on one planet. We need to care for that planet and take responsibility for it. But we also need to progress with the search for new homes and the technology to take us to the stars.

Galileo   **Stillman Drake**

Galileo's significance for the formation of modern science lies partly in his discoveries and opinions in physics and astronomy, but much more in his refusal to allow science to be guided any longer by philosophy. By stages, his rejection of the long-established authority of philosophers induced them to appeal to the Bible for support, and there ensued a battle for freedom of scientific enquiry which profoundly affected the development of modern society, leading to a final parting of the ways between science and philosophy. In a startling reinterpretation of the evidence, Stillman Drake advances the hypothesis that Galileo's trial and condemnation by the Inquisition in 1633 was caused not by his defiance of the Church, but by the hostility of contemporary philosophers.

Darwin   **Jonathan Howard**

Focusing on Darwin's major insights and arguments, Jonathan Howard reasserts the importance of Darwin's work for the development of modern science and culture.

Darwin's contribution to biology

The whole point of understanding the modern theory of evolution is to understand that human life and human society are to a certain extent biological issues, painfully difficult to deal with in these terms, but still biology. For this reason, this introduction keeps strictly to the core of the matter, which is Darwin's contribution to biology. Darwinian philosophy or Darwinian society are *post-hoc* constructs that had no place in Darwin's thought. He was unable to see how evolution in biology could have any but the feeblest analogical resemblance to the evolution of society. The complete separation between social and political philosophy and Darwin's Darwinism is the main justification, if any is needed, for dealing only with the latter. The biology is where the issues are finally grounded, and it is probably the biology that is least generally known.

Evolution   **Brian and Deborah Charlesworth**

> We are all one with creeping things;
> And apes and men
> Blood-brethren.
>
> From *Drinking Song*, Thomas Hardy

What can we learn from evolution?

Science tells us that human beings are the product of impersonal forces, and that the habitable world forms a minute part of a universe of immense size and duration. Whatever the religious or philosophical beliefs of individual scientists, the whole programme of scientific research is founded on the assumption that the universe can be understood on such a basis.

Few would dispute that this programme has been spectacularly successful, particularly in the 20th century, which saw such terrible events in human affairs. The influence of science may have indirectly contributed to these events, partly through the social changes triggered by the rise of industrial mass societies, and partly through the undermining of traditional belief systems.

The study of evolution has revealed our intimate connections with the other species that inhabit the earth. The purpose of this book is to introduce the reader to some of the most important basic findings, concepts, and procedures of evolutionary biology, as it has developed since the first publications of Darwin and Wallace on the subject, over 140 years ago. Evolution provides a set of unifying principles for the whole of biology; it also illuminates the relation of human beings to the universe and to each other.

Philosophy of Science   **Samir Okasha**

Samir Okasha investigates the nature of scientific reasoning, scientific explanation, revolutions in science, and theories such as realism and anti-realism.

Why is this important?

Scientific ideas change fast. Pick virtually any scientific discipline, and you can be sure that the prevalent theories in that discipline will be very different from those of 50 years ago, and extremely different from those of 100 years ago. A number of interesting philosophical questions centre on the issue of scientific change. Is there a discernible pattern to the way scientific ideas change over time? When scientists abandon their existing theory in favour of a new one, how should we explain this? Are later scientific theories objectively better than earlier ones? Or does the concept of objectivity make sense at all?

> *'This book gives an excellent sense of what keeps philosophers of science awake at night. The issues and the arguments are presented with stunning clarity.'*
>
> Peter Lipton, University of Cambridge

Forthcoming
Molecules, Philip Ball

Chapter 2
There's more to us
than meets the eye

Introduction   **Simon Blackburn**

There are theorems in logic that as you ascend to do the theory of
a theory, you need more powerful methods and get less solid results
than if you stay down below. The same kind of result applies to
writing a very short introduction to Very Short Introductions. Yet
anyone browsing these amazing little books will recognize that
philosophy lends itself ideally to very short introductions. For apart
from dry and dedicated specialists, few people remember anything
more of even favourite philosophers than some very short sound
bites.

Philosophy may or may not be as Milton described it: 'a perpetual
feast of nectar'd sweets, where no crude surfeit reigns'. It is arguably
unique among subjects in that a lot of its practitioners spend a lot of
their time wondering what it is. Is it an art or a science? Does it
discover things in the sense of uncovering truths that were always
waiting to be revealed? Or does it discover things in the sense in
which someone might discover a new way to entertain teenagers, or
play King Lear? Should it aspire to the condition of mathematics,
or the condition of music: truth, entertainment, or something else
again?

Traditionally, philosophy means reflection on some concepts that
structure a lot of our thought – big concepts, such as truth, reason,
objectivity, knowledge, goodness, God, the soul, freedom, virtue,
and meaning. And it means studying the writers whose reflections

on those big concepts have been important, or still speak to us now. But after that, things become less clear. Why do some concepts, but not others, get on to the list? And what distinguishes the philosopher from the mere preacher, on the one hand, and from the other people licensed to reflect upon the human condition, such as writers of fiction, poets, and dramatists, on the other hand? Admittedly, the dividing lines are sometimes thin, since some philosophers, such as Plato or Nietzsche, are rather like poets, and others, such as Marx or Engels or Augustine, are frequently not so far from being preachers. Rousseau wrote novels, and Hume wrote excellent dialogue. Perhaps there is no way of drawing a sharp boundary. If someone reflects about how things hang together, in the most general sense of the term, perhaps that is enough to qualify them as a philosopher.

But then what does reflection mean here? A philosopher is neither a laboratory scientist, nor a social scientist armed with a clipboard or a set of statistics. Some philosophers, especially in the contemporary world, like to think of themselves as closely allied to the natural sciences, and some, such as Descartes, have been distinguished natural scientists themselves. But the lack of experimental practice makes the alliance with natural science a bit suspect, to say the least. It is as if the philosopher sets himself up as a maker of maps who needs to make no observations and take no measurements. For Kant, this was the central puzzle in the whole theory of knowledge. The possibility that the mind, by simple self-conscious reflection, should obtain knowledge about its own nature and the nature of its world was sufficiently strange to require the *Critique of Pure Reason* to lay it to rest.

Unfortunately, not even Kant's 800 pages could do that. A definitive story of the scope and limits of human reflection would tell us, for instance, whether there is progress in philosophy, and, if not, why we are condemned to trudge permanently around the same maze. For Hegel there is indeed progress, and the whole of human history is the progress of a kind of self-consciousness. Although as Peter

Singer engagingly points out in his contribution on Hegel, the German word *Selbstbewusstsein* has more the flavour of self-assertion than the English word self-consciousness, with its hint of introspection or even embarrassment, and it is perhaps easier to see history as a progress of human beings throwing their weight about rather than a progress of anything more contemplative.

In his book in this series, *Philosophy: A Very Short Introduction* Edward Craig reminds us how natural it is to human beings to find themselves reflecting on their world, and the success or failure of their pursuits, and the hidden forces to which they might appeal to do better. Philosophies of life try to systematize these answers, most obviously in the texts that form the basis of religious systems. Religion is the first expression of the philosophical impulse. Science is the second, and it is of course a first-rate philosophical question whether it supersedes and displaces the first, or whether it can live alongside it. We will write the history of self-consciousness very differently according to how we answer this question.

If philosophy were like religion, then it might decay, and if it were like mathematics, only done with words, it might progress. Perhaps the best answer strips Hegel of his confidence, and contents itself with allowing that in so far as humanity progresses, so will philosophy progress with it, and in so far as humanity merely changes, so will philosophy merely change with it. My own *Ethics: A Very Short Introduction* supposes that subjectivism and relativism, as well as misapplications of evolutionary and biological theory, get in the way of ethical thinking, now more than ever. Here, we may actually have gone backwards.

Where does philosophy stand now? And where is it going? If we suppose, with Hegel, Marx, or Foucault, that philosophical reflection is always motivated by general cultural forces and anxieties, then it will be a question of what bothers us now, and will bother us in the future. It is difficult enough to answer the first.

Indeed, it is impossible if we add the doctrine that those anxieties are standardly unconscious, so that at some deep level the concerns and the presuppositions of any particular time only become visible at another time, as self-consciousness distances itself from them. To take an example almost at random, as Julia Annas describes in her *Ancient Philosophy: A Very Short Introduction*, we can see the Victorians as anxious about government, and hence anxious to portray Plato as a kind of godfather of the civil service. But they were not themselves aware that this is what they were doing, or they could not have done it. Once it is self-conscious, the ideology becomes embarrassed.

In such a picture, the philosopher merely follows the parade. As Hegel put it, the owl of Minerva only takes wing with the coming of the night. But this seems wrong as well, for, after all, the literature of a time not only reflects that time, but helps mould the self-awareness and identity of those who follow and read it. We have only to think of Marx, or of the struggles of feminist writers to articulate an ideology, and their political successes when they did so. To paraphrase Nietzsche, ideas are explosions waiting to happen. But as for where philosophy is going, if this picture is right, we cannot predict that any more than we can predict the future. As is often said, if we could predict inventions, we would invent them. To have predicted a great philosopher would have been to have thought what he did before him, and then he wouldn't have been a great philosopher.

Philosophy and the philosophers described in this series give us a world literature. We don't know where literature is going. What we do know is how exciting it is to see where it has been. It is remarkable to have a resource giving us so much awareness of that, and one asking for such little effort from the reader.

Philosophy   **Edward Craig**

Philosophy is not an activity from another planet: learning about it is just a matter of broadening and deepening what most of us do already. In this lively and engaging book, Edward Craig shows that philosophy is no mere intellectual pastime; thinkers such as Plato, Descartes, Hegel, Darwin, Mill, and de Beauvoir, and Buddhist writers, were responding to real needs and events – much of their work shapes our lives today, and many of their concerns are still ours.

Anyone reading this book is to some extent a philosopher already. Nearly all of us are, because we have some kinds of values by which we live our lives (or like to think we do, or feel uncomfortable when we don't). And most of us favour some very general picture of what the world is like. Perhaps we think there's a god who made it all, including us; or, on the contrary, we think it's all a matter of chance and natural selection. Perhaps we believe that people have immortal, non-material parts called souls or spirits; or, quite the opposite, that we are just complicated arrangements of matter that gradually fall to bits after we die. So most of us, even those who don't *think about it* at all, have something like answers to the two basic philosophical questions, namely: what should we do? and, what is there?

> 'A vigorous and engaging introduction that speaks to the philosopher in everyone. Craig helps the reader grapple with some key texts and problems are carefully chosen to show how philosophical inquiry is something we should all care about.'
>
> John Cottingham, University of Reading

3. Cartoon from *Punch*.

Ancient Philosophy   Julia Annas

Getting away from the presentation of ancient philosophy as a
succession of Great Thinkers, this book aims to give readers a sense
of the freshness and liveliness of ancient philosophy, and of its wide
variety of themes and styles.

The pursuit of a happy life

Happiness in ancient ethical thought is not a matter of feeling good
or being pleased; it is not a feeling or emotion at all. It is your life as
a whole which is said to be happy or not, and so discussions of
happiness are discussions of the happy life. It is our bad luck that
for us what is happy are not just lives, but also moments and
fleeting experiences; modern discussions of happiness tend to get
confused very rapidly because such different things are being
considered. In ancient ethics, happiness enters by a very different
route from the 'feel-good' one.

'Incisive, elegant, and full of the excitement of doing philosophy, [this book] boldly steps outside the conventional chronological ways of organizing material about the Greeks and Romans to get right to the heart of the human problems that exercised them ... I can't think of a better way to begin.'

Martha Nussbaum, University of Chicago

Continental Philosophy   **Simon Critchley**

The author tells a story that begins with the publication of Kant's critical philosophy in the 1780s and includes discussions of major philosophers like Nietzsche, Heidegger, Foucault, and Kristeva. At the core of the book is a plea to place philosophy at the centre of cultural life, and thereby reawaken its primary definition of the love of wisdom that makes life worth living.

Principal strands of continental philosophy

1) German idealism and romanticism, and their aftermath (Fichte, Schelling, Hegel, Schlegel and Novalis, Schleiermacher, Schopenhauer)

2) The critique of metaphysics and the 'masters of suspicion' (Feuerbach, Marx, Nietzsche, Freud, Bergson)

3) Germanophone phenomenology and existential philosophy (Husserl, Max Scheler, Karl Jaspers, Heidegger)

4) French phenomenology, Hegelianism and anti-Hegelianism (Kojève, Sartre, Merleau-Ponty, Levinas, Bataille, de Beauvoir)

5) Hermeneutics (Dilthey, Gadamer, Ricoeur)

6) Western Marxism and the Frankfurt School (Lukács, Benjamin, Horkheimer, Adorno, Marcuse, Habermas)

7) French structuralism (Lévi-Strauss, Lacan, Althusser), post-structuralism (Foucault, Derrida, Deleuze), post-modernism (Lyotard, Baudrillard), and feminism (Irigaray, Kristeva)

Indian Philosophy   Sue Hamilton

From the earliest beginnings, philosophical debate in India developed, flourished, and proliferated into a variety of schools of thought. In highlighting its key features, the author draws the reader into the world of 'classical' Indian philosophy, illustrating the different ways in which the great Indian thinkers interpreted and sought to understand the nature of reality.

Understanding Indian philosophy

Westerners approaching the Indian tradition for the first time, whether their interest be primarily in religion or in philosophy, are faced with two equal and opposing problems. One is to find something graspable amid the apparently bewildering multiplicity; the other is not enforcing such a straitjacket on to the material as to overlook significant aspects of the diversity. The classic example of the latter is 'Hinduism': because of the existence of the name Hinduism, Westerners expect to find a monolithic tradition comparable to other 'isms'. They remain baffled by what they find until they discover that Hinduism is a label that was attached in the 19th century to a highly complex and multiple collection of systems of thought by other Westerners who did not appreciate that complexity.

Animal Rights   **David DeGrazia**

Do animals have moral rights? If so, what does this mean? What sorts of mental lives do animals have, and how should we understand their welfare? After putting forward possible answers to these questions, David DeGrazia explores the implications for how we treat animals in connection with our diet, zoos, and research.

Do animals have souls?

One common contention is that animals lack awareness or consciousness because they lack *immortal souls*, conceived as immaterial substances. But this is an extremely weak argument. It ignores all empirical evidence for animal awareness while resting on an assumption for which there is no basis: that human beings but no other animals possess immortal souls. One wonders when exactly in hominid evolution our ancestors began to have souls!

Choice Theory   **Michael Allingham**

We make choices all the time. We also constantly judge the decisions that other people make as rational or irrational. But what kinds of criteria are we applying when we say that a choice is rational, and what guides our own choices, especially in cases where we do not have complete information about the possible outcomes? This book explores what it means to be rational in all these contexts and shows that life is about making choices.

Choose rationally

> Choose life. Choose a job ... Choose a big television ... Choose good health, low cholesterol and dental insurance. Choose fixed-interest mortgage repayments ... Choose your friends. Choose your future ... Choose life.

All choices, just as Renton's opening voiceover (above) from the film *Trainspotting*, arise from both the heart and the head. But is he

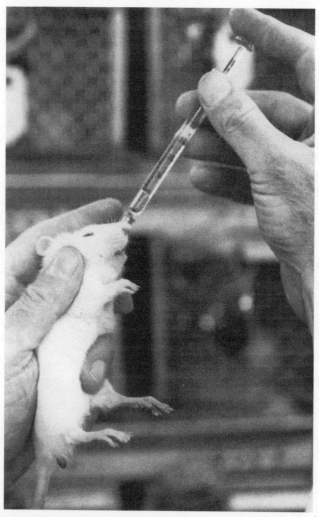

4. A mouse undergoing a laboratory procedure.

choosing rationally? The heart provides the passion and the head the reasons. Choices based on the most minute reasoning but lacking any desire are vacuous, while desire without reason is impotent: it is only fit for the enraged child who wants both to go home and not to go home. Aristotle, the founder of choice theory, and indeed of logic itself, identifies the connection:

> 'The origin of . . . choice is desire and reasoning with a view to the end – this is why choice cannot exist without . . . reason.'

Words of wisdom from VSI

These classic, readable introductions to philosophers' lives and works, previously published as *Past Masters*, are now available in the Very Short Introductions series.

Aristotle   **Jonathan Barnes**

Politicians have no leisure because they are always aiming at something beyond political life itself, power and glory, or happiness.

Plato   **Julia Annas**

Is that which is holy loved by the gods because it is holy, or is it holy because it is loved by the gods?

Socrates   **C. C. W. Taylor**

The unexamined life is not worth living.

Augustine   **Henry Chadwick**

Take up and read, take up and read.

Hobbes   **Richard Tuck**

Laughter is nothing else but sudden glory arising from some sudden conception of some eminency in ourselves, by comparison with the infirmity of others, or with our own formerly.

Descartes   **Tom Sorell**

Common sense is the best distributed commodity in the world, for every man is convinced that he is well supplied with it.

Spinoza   **Roger Scruton**

So far as in me lies, I value, above all other things out of my control, the joining hands of friendship with men who are lovers of truth.

Locke   **John Dunn**

New opinions are always suspected, and usually opposed, without any other reason but because they are not already common.

Hume   **A. J. Ayer**

The heart of man is made to reconcile the most glaring of contradictions.

Rousseau — Robert Wokler

Everything is good when it springs from the hands of our Creator; everything degenerates when shaped by the hands of man.

Kant — Roger Scruton

Many people imagine that the years of their youth are the pleasantest and best of their lives; but it is not really so. They are the most troublesome; for we are then under strict discipline, can seldom choose our friends, and still more seldom have our freedom.

Hegel — Peter Singer

What experience and history can tell us is this – that nations and governments have never learned anything from history, or acted upon any lessons they might have drawn from it.

Clausewitz — Michael Howard

War is nothing but a continuation of politics with the admixture of other means.

Schopenhauer — Christopher Janaway

The word of man is the most durable of all material.

Kierkegaard — Patrick Gardiner

An honest religious thinker is like a tightrope walker. He almost looks as though he were walking on nothing but air. His support is the slenderest imaginable. And yet it really is possible to walk on it.

Marx   **Peter Singer**

The philosophers have only interpreted the world in various ways; the point is to change it.

Engels   **Terrell Carver**

Naturally, the workers are perfectly free; the manufacturer does not force them to take his materials and his cards, but he says to them: 'If you don't like to be frizzled in my frying-pan, you can take a walk into the fire.'

Nietzsche   **Michael Tanner**

What I understand by 'philosopher': a terrible explosive in the presence of which everything is in danger.

Russell   **A. C. Grayling**

Every man, wherever he goes, is encompassed by a cloud of comforting convictions, which move with him like flies on a summer day.

Wittgenstein   **A. C. Grayling**

Philosophy is a battle against the bewitchment of our intelligence by means of language.

Heidegger   **Michael Inwood**

Beauty is a fateful gift of the essence of truth, and here truth means the disclosure of what keeps itself concealed.

Chapter 3
What can the past tell us?

Introduction   Mary Beard

A quotation from ancient Rome's most famous poet sits in the pockets and purses, tills and collecting boxes, of most people in Britain. Around the edge of the English one pound coin are engraved three Latin words: 'decus et tutamen', 'an ornament and a protection' – or (as the Bank of England would like you to think) 'something that looks nice and something you can rely on'. This slogan has been a feature of British coinage for hundreds of years. It was apparently suggested by the 17th-century diarist John Evelyn, who claimed to have got it from Cardinal Richelieu. But its first appearance was 2,000 years ago in Virgil's monumental epic poem, the *Aeneid* – his grand re-telling of the story of the foundation of the Eternal City, a classic meditation on the nature of political power and leadership. Halfway through the narrative, the hero Aeneas launches some lavish games to mark the funeral of his father. One of the events is a boat race, and the prize for the man who took second place is a piece of armour, a breast-plate interwoven with gold: 'decus et tutamen' as Virgil put it.

Why on earth the second prize in an ancient rowing competition (the first prize was a rather more splendid cloak) should make its mark so firmly on British coinage is just the kind of question that drives Very Short Introductions. And these ancient echoes are not just a quirk of British culture and coinage. The slogan on the United States' dollar bill – 'e pluribus unum', 'one [state] made out of many' – is itself taken from an even more unlikely ancient source:

the recipe for a salad in a poem also thought to have been written by Virgil. The modern Greek two euro piece actually features an image of the frankly misogynistic ancient myth of the rape of Europa, carried off by the god Zeus in the shape of a bull. It makes the starting point for Helen Morales's exciting, fresh look at the uses of classical mythology in the contemporary world, in her forthcoming *Classical Myth: A Very Short Introduction*. But if the ancient world jangles in all our pockets, it also confronts us from stage and screen, from hoardings and textbooks, novels and posters, low and high art. From the mummy's curse to the decipherment of hieroglyphs (two new VSIs focus on ancient Egypt and hieroglyphic writing), from TV's *Gladiator* to Freud's Oedipus complex and modern feminism, Very Short Introductions look at what the ancient world was all about and why it still matters to us now.

Asking the right questions

Classics: A Very Short Introduction was the first in the whole series; and, as an inaugural volume, it made clear (or so I like to imagine) that no introduction to anything about the modern world could be complete without an introduction to Classics. We did not set out to write the history of Greece and Rome, or of the 'classics' of Greek and Latin literature that are still read, performed, and enjoyed today (though plenty of that comes in *en route*). Nor was it a question of simply explaining how ancient Greece and Rome have impacted on our own world (though there is some fond discussion of T. S. Eliot, Asterix, Louis MacNeice, and Nigel Molesworth). We wanted to open up all that territory that lies between us and the ancient world itself – the story that goes back beyond the everyday coin of the 21st century, through Evelyn and Richelieu to Virgil himself. And we wanted to show how and why the classical world, along with its inheritance, is still worth arguing about. Mussolini's attempts to re-figure himself as the first Roman emperor Augustus, Karl Marx's training in Greek philosophy, or Freud's reading of Greek myth still matter; as does the hot topic of where, and to whom, the Parthenon marbles belong, or whether Greek democracy offers a useful model for our own beleaguered political systems.

If the languages of Greece and Rome are in one sense 'dead', the study of Classics is never a *post mortem*. It lies somewhere at the root of pretty much everything that we can say, see, or think within Western culture. Or so *Classics: A Very Short Introduction* tries to show.

The same could be said of Paul Bahn's *Archaeology: A Very Short Introduction*. He offers a hard look at what remnants of antiquity archaeologists actually dig out of the ground; but he also presents a wry angle on the arguments that rage on how all this material is to be interpreted. It is an engaging entry-point to the fierce debates between archaeologists the world over on what all the traces of flint and shards of pottery really can tell us about how ancient societies worked and lived. One of the most revealing cartoons in the book (which is illustrated throughout with some hilarious gems from Bill Tidy and others) pictures a group of professional archaeologists in the course of an 'academic argument' (Figure 5): as one of the archaeologists biffs another with a placard reading 'Burn all Neo-Marxist heretics', and another retorts by shouting 'Phallocrat scum-bag', the Joe Public family (who have just come to visit an attractive heritage site on a Sunday afternoon out) retreat in horror and confusion at the scene. Bahn's book is a wonderfully funny – and also informative – attempt to explain what might be going on in these kinds of disputes. What is it that archaeologists discuss in such heated tones? How do they argue about how to make sense of the traces of ancient culture they dig up? And what difference does it make for the rest of us, who might only want to put a name and a date to the scant ruins or the fragments in the museum case?

The same kind of focus is promised by Ian Shaw's *Ancient Egypt: A Very Short Introduction*, in which we shall be introduced to the culture, art, mythology, and religion of Egyptian society, millennia ago – but will also reflect on the impact Ancient Egypt has made on our own world. Why are we so ghoulishly fascinated by mummies? Is there a 'Tomb Raider' in all of us?

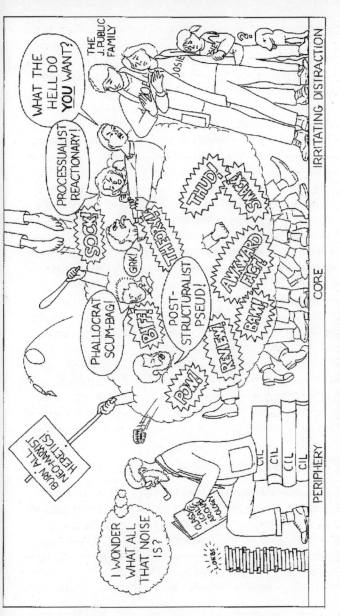

5. An 'academic argument' among professional archaeologists.

Classics   **Mary Beard and John Henderson**

Classics can itself be *good to think with* – as well as fun. Again and again, imaginative entertainments and instructive re-creations explore Greek and Roman culture to find orientation for our own world, and to offer opportunities to fantasize. Cleopatras of all sorts – on the page, the stage, or celluloid – from Claudette Colbert to Elizabeth Taylor, have brought the European West a compelling series of visions of the seductions and perversions of the Orient, plus the irresistible formula that ensures that the dominance of Cleopatra over the captivated Mark Anthony is always in the end cancelled out by her death; the story always ends with the restoration of proper political order and male supremacy. On the other hand, in the *Asterix* cartoon-strips the tables are turned on the powerful, as the last remnants in the last corner of a free Gaul magically overpower the legions of Caesar, mock the dull wits and flabby physiques of his officers and soldiers, and in the end return to their 'Arcadian' village to feast and sup as (the myth lies) they always will.

> *'You could not find two better introducers to the Classics than Mary Beard and John Henderson. They are questioning, funny, bold, and widely read in many fields. They could not be dull if they tried.'*
>
> The Times

Archaeology   **Paul Bahn**

To the general public, archaeology tends to be synonymous with digging, as if this is what practitioners of the subject do all the time. In the British satirical magazine *Private Eye*, any archaeologist is automatically described as 'man with beard in hole'. Cartoons usually depict archaeologists as crusty old fogeys, covered in cobwebs, and obsessed with old bones and cracked pots. Of course, all of this is perfectly accurate, but it only reflects a very small part of the subject. Some archaeologists never excavate, for example, and very few of them spend most of their time at it. Archaeology can provide a window on the last 2.5 million years and help us reconstruct a past that holds a great deal of fascination for us.

Gruesome discoveries

Archaeology can reveal the lives of our distant ancestors, often highlighting the trauma and damage their bodies suffered. Many of the preserved bog bodies of northwest Europe clearly met violent deaths, generally as a result of executions, muggings, or ritual sacrifices. Tollund Man was hanged, Grauballe Man had his throat slit, but Britain's Lindow Man – wittily nicknamed Pete Marsh – takes the biscuit: he had his skull fractured twice, was garotted, and had his jugular cut. Either he was extremely unpopular, or someone was determined to do a very thorough job.

6. The mummified body of a man, buried in a peat bog at Lindow, Cheshire.

The most intact body to have come down to us is that of the Iceman, found in the Italian Alps in 1991. His discovery attracted worldwide attention in the media, and immediately triggered some amazing stories, some of them probably apocryphal. For example, one woman claimed the body was her father, who had disappeared in the mountains – she recognized him from the press photographs! The radiocarbon dates of 5,300 years ago soon put paid to that one. Once he had been identified as a genuinely ancient individual, some women allegedly volunteered to be impregnated with any frozen sperm that might be found in his body.

'a quite brilliant and level-headed look at the curious world of archaeology.'

Barry Cunliffe, University of Oxford

Social and Cultural Anthropology
John Monaghan and Peter Just

Anthropology grew out of the intersection of European discovery, colonialism, and natural science. In the 19th century the first anthropologists, influenced by the same philosophical currents that led to the Darwinian revolution, were interested in reconstructing stages of social and cultural evolution. Influential works were published tracing everything from writing systems to marriage practices from their most primitive origins to their modern manifestations. By the beginning of the last century, anthropologists had developed other intellectual projects and, most importantly, were no longer content to rely on the accounts of colonial officials, missionaries, travellers, and other non-specialists for their primary data. They began to go into the 'field' as ethnographers to gather their own information first hand. Although anthropology has changed quite a bit since the time of these ethnographic pioneers, ethnography remains one of the things that distinguishes anthropology from the rest of the social sciences, and the importance of doing ethnography is perhaps the one thing that all anthropologists agree upon.

When out in the field

Being in the field can often put the anthropologist in challenging situations. One of the authors, John Monaghan, tells how he was invited to go hunting with several of his Mixtec friends.

Toward the end of the day I was following my friends up the side of a ridge. They were well ahead of me, and when I finally reached the top I could see them crouched around something at the base of a tree and talking excitedly. As I approached, I saw it was a beehive, which one of them knocked down with a stick. When it hit the ground it split open, revealing a mass of comb, honey, and bee larvae. My three friends were busy tearing out pieces of the hive – including those containing the bee larvae – and popping them into their mouths. One of them suddenly stood up and said 'Wait, we're being impolite.' He reached down into the hive and pulled out a big glob of comb, honey, and squiggling bee larvae. He then turned to me and said, while holding out his hand, 'Here, John, this is all for you.' Seeing no way to refuse him, I took it from him, held my breath, put it in my mouth and swallowed.

What can the past tell us?

Forthcoming
Classical Myth, Helen Morales
Ancient Egypt, Ian Shaw
Hieroglyphs, Penelope Wilson
Ancient Warfare, Harry Sidebottom

Chapter 4
Are there any good guys?

Introduction   **Stephen Howe**

This is a strange, but on the whole a very good, time for anyone interested in history. There is a pervasive intellectual self-doubt over whether it is possible to do history at all. Can we ever have any certain knowledge about what has happened in the past? What, if anything, can it mean to be 'objective', 'unbiased', or 'impartial'? Is there even such a thing as historical 'truth'? Some academic historians, beset by such doubts, start to resemble the proverbial figure of the man busily sawing away at the very branch on which he is sitting.

Yet, history is enormously popular – maybe more so than at any time in the past. History books, including ones of the utmost seriousness, based on massive research, feature regularly in the bestseller lists of almost all countries; history is the only kind of intelligent non-fiction that regularly challenges the popular novel and the lifestyle manual in this respect. Never before has television devoted so much time to historical documentaries and dramas; there are digital and satellite channels dedicated entirely to the subject. Family history research is among the most prevalent and fastest-growing of all leisure pursuits. Millions of people visit historical museums, old buildings, and other 'heritage sites' every weekend. Millions more collect everything from old coins to historic militaria, or decorate and furnish their homes and themselves with different kinds of 'retrochic'. Re-enactment societies vie with local archaeological groups in their apparent omnipresence. All these, and many more, are manifestations of a genuine mass-based passion for history, however much some scholars may scorn them.

We should also, surely, be impressed by the sheer variety of interests involved. Some people, it's true, are obsessed only with their own family's story – or with legends about it. Most historical research, whether professional or amateur, sticks closely to the investigator's own region or country. Most of the history that is formally taught in schools and colleges, in almost every country, is still national in focus. Some commentators seem convinced that people only ever want to read or hear about 'their own kind': Women's History for women only, Black History for black people, and so on. But the historical fascinations that are revealed in people's spontaneous choice of reading are, encouragingly, far more diverse and less predictable than that (despite those ubiquitous Nazis). Often, it is precisely the most alien or unfamiliar which is most engaging. Ever more readers are curious about a *global* past, not just a local or national one. History Very Short Introductions reflect that breadth and diversity. Alongside a strong list of titles in British history, there are many recent or forthcoming books on global themes: Charles Townshend on *Terrorism*, Michael Howard's *The First World War*, John Parker and Richard Rathbone on *African History*, or my own *Empire*.

In a quite different register, states and politicians are obviously convinced that history matters, and always have been so convinced. No subject is so intensely political. In countries as diverse as Australia and Israel, Germany and India – just to mention a few of those where bitter disputes are raging as I write – competing views about national histories are at the heart of controversy over the very meaning of nationhood. Communities in conflict sustain themselves, and seek to justify their causes, with their rival versions of history – as in modern Ireland, and especially in the North, subjects of VSIs by Senia Pašeta and Marc Mulholland. Not only does the study of history almost always carry a powerful political and moral charge, but the very concept of 'politics', or such key values as 'democracy', can only be understood historically: VSIs by Kenneth Minogue and Bernard Crick, respectively, on those themes make that point with both force and verve.

History, then, is quite generally felt to carry both moral and political authority. Yet its appeal is not confined to so deadly serious a level. People turn to historians wanting to learn, to seek guidance about burning contemporary issues and perennial puzzles of the human heart. But they also seek entertainment, and no other serious intellectual field has such innate potential to entertain as does history. Its capacity to surprise, to offer the 'shock of the new' by looking with fresh eyes at the old, is almost unlimited. Personally, I have found myself pleasurably startled out of my previous assumptions by VSIs on subjects with which I'd thought I was almost wearily familiar, like Kevin Passmore's on *Fascism* or John Pinder's on the *The European Union*.

History students are, very early in their studies, routinely admonished that they should avoid narrative and go for an analytical approach instead. But a great deal of history's appeal lies precisely in the sphere of narrative, and there is no reason to be snobbish about that. Story-telling is among the oldest of all human activities – one of the most universal, one of the most demanding. So several of the History VSIs – like the splendid series which now covers almost the entire sweep of British history, from Peter Salway's *Roman Britain* to Kenneth Morgan on the 20th century, or like William Doyle and S. A. Smith on the French and Russian Revolutions – offer clear, vigorous narratives, telling us what happened, to whom, and when. John Arnold's *History: A Very Short Introduction* itself urges the point that history is, at bottom, about individuals, what they did and what was done to them – and Arnold illustrates this with some dazzling vignettes of his own.

But, of course, 'narrative' and 'analysis' are not really opposites. All these books offer something more than a good story well told. They work hard at explaining why things happened, or why people believed what they did – or, for that matter, where necessary, why historians can't agree about such issues. All of them reflect and try to summarize many years' hard thinking on their subjects by the authors. And they invite the reader to think hard about them too.

History   **John H. Arnold**

Do historians reconstruct the truth or simply tell stories? John Arnold suggests that they do both, and that the balance between 'truth' and 'story' is tremendously important to history. Taking us from the fabulous tales of ancient Greek historians to the varied approaches of modern historians, he illuminates our relationship to the past by making us aware of how 'history' has changed as a subject. Concepts such as periodization and causation are discussed through particular historical examples that illustrate the ways in which we understand history, giving the reader a sense of the excitement of discovering not only the past, but also something about ourselves.

Evidence and interpretation

Historians, like everyone else, can misread, misremember, misinterpret, or misunderstand things. Every historical account has gaps, problems, contradictions, areas of uncertainty. An author of fiction can invent people, places, and happenings, whereas a historian is bound by what the evidence will support. For every historian, what is at stake is what actually happened – and what it might *mean*. There is an excitement to these precarious attempts to grasp the 'truth', a truth that might at any point be revealed as illusory.

Lessons from the past?

To imagine that there are concrete patterns to past events, which can provide templates for our lives and decisions, is to project on to history a hope for a certainty which it cannot fulfil. Studying history necessarily involves taking oneself out of one's present context and exploring an alternative world. To see how people have behaved in the past offers us an opportunity to think about how we behave, to think about the things we take for granted; history throws us into stark relief.

> *'His range of knowledge and interests is phenomenal, but his skill as a communicator makes his own subtle analysis of history's history as gripping as a novel.'*

Neal Ascherson

Prehistory   **Chris Gosden**

A prehistoric site

The activities of a group of early people and animals at Boxgrove, near Chichester in southern England, half a million years ago can be reconstructed using archaeology. None of the creatures involved had the remotest awareness that traces of their activities would survive for half a million years, preserved by rapid burial under collapsing cliff sediments. No words survive to tell us of this and countless other incidents, but we can give voice to questions aplenty. Beautifully detailed excavation and recording of the site has shown six (or perhaps seven) discrete areas of flint working where hand axes were fashioned. Dealing with a three-dimensional jigsaw puzzle, archaeologists have worked in reverse order to the earlier hominids – rather than breaking down a big nodule of flint into small flakes and a large hand axe, they have put the flakes back together again to create a complete nodule with only one missing element, the hand axe itself. A void is left in the centre of the stone, reminding us that in some parts of the world more recent stone knappers have seen their task as not making a stone tool, but rather freeing it from its encasing stone material. Once freed, these particular hand axes have so far eluded archaeological detection, although they may lie in another part of the same site, discarded by a meat-bloated creature moving off to rest somewhere safe. Indeed, many dozens of near-pristine hand axes have been recovered from Boxgrove, some with microscopic traces that indicate they were used for butchery.

When was prehistory?

The above indicates what prehistory might be, but has not tackled the question of when it was. Boxgrove provides a window into the deep past of Britain. As chance would have it, prehistory ended when Julius Caesar landed on the south coast not that many miles away from Boxgrove.

The Renaissance   Jerry Brotton

In Western Europe, the word 'Renaissance' immediately conjures up images of places like Florence and Venice, and the great artists and thinkers of the 15th and 16th centuries – Leonardo, Michelangelo, Copernicus, and Shakespeare. It's an intoxicating and deeply persuasive idea that has held sway for nearly two centuries. This book challenges these deeply held assumptions by arguing that they were invented in the 19th century by a group of historians who had little interest in the more global and multicultural influences that actually underpinned the foundations of the Renaissance. In fact, the very term 'renaissance' was invented by historians like Jules Michelet and Jacob Burckhardt in the 19th century; nobody in the 15th century would have identified themselves as living through a 'renaissance' in the way that we see ourselves as living in the 'modern world'.

Rather than Florence, Rome, and Venice, it was places to the east of Europe – Constantinople, Baghdad, Cairo, Damascus, and the bazaars of North Africa and the Middle East – that made crucial contributions to the Renaissance world. The wealth of luxury objects that Europe bought from the east – spices, silk, porcelain, gems, horses, even pigments for painting – all contributed to the extraordinary transformation in art, taste, and cultural life that we now call the European Renaissance. As well as objects, new ideas in science and the arts were openly and amicably exchanged with Arabic and Islamic cultures to Europe's east. Developments in algebra, astronomy, anatomy, finance, even the word for 'cheque', all resulted from European merchants and artists travelling to the east and learning new ideas, which were slowly but profoundly absorbed into the European way of life.

Traditionally, one of the most traumatic moments in Renaissance history was the fall of Constantinople in 1453 to the Ottoman Turks and their feared sultan, Mehmed II, subsequently called 'The Conqueror'. Constantinople was the eastern seat of Christendom and the 1,000-year-old Byzantine Empire, and the Papacy was horrified at its loss to the Muslim Turks. In fact, after taking the city, Mehmed became one of the most generous and discerning patrons of his day. In the early 16th century, as Nicolaus Copernicus developed his revolutionary heliocentric theory of the solar system (arguing that the earth revolved around the sun), he borrowed his basic ideas about planetary motion from the discoveries of 13th-century Persian astronomers. Even Shakespeare showed his fascination with the east in the earliest plays he wrote, such as *Comedy of Errors* (set in the Middle East), an interest that ran all the way through to *Othello* and *The Tempest* – which is, after all, set on an island somewhere off the coast of Tunisia!

Today, following the events of 11th September 2001, and the gloomy discussions of the 'clash of civilisations', we should remember that the defining moment of Europe's emergence into the modern world occurred because of an open and often friendly exchange of objects and ideas with the east. We should learn from our past in rejecting the fear and cultural intolerance that threatens to overwhelm our present, not to mention our future.

> *'A young Turk who likes to entertain ... This is a Renaissance you can touch and feel'*
>
> Sunday Times

British history in VSIs

Eight leading experts chart the history of Britain in a concise and highly readable way in this group of titles based on the bestselling *Oxford Illustrated History of Britain*.

Roman Britain   Peter Salway

Britain was within the orbit of Graeco-Roman civilization for at least half a millennium, and for over 350 years was part of the political union created by the Roman Empire that encompassed most of Europe and all the countries of the Mediterranean. Here, the author weaves together the results of archaeological investigation and historical scholarship to chart the history of Britain from the first invasion under Julius Caesar to the final collapse of the Romano-British way of life in the 5th century AD.

> *'Highly readable, attractively illustrated, admirably succinct, yet with the odd surprise even for the comparatively well-informed.'*
>
> The Scotsman

The Anglo-Saxon Age   John Blair

Covering the period from the earliest English settlements to the Norman victory in 1066, this book is a brief introduction to the political, social, religious, and cultural history of an age when so many basic aspects of modern England were formed: its language, governmental institutions, rural landscape, communications, and towns.

Medieval Britain John Gillingham and Ralph A. Griffiths

The establishment of the Anglo-Norman monarchy in the early Middle Ages, through to England's failure to dominate the British Isles and France in the later Middle Ages, provide the historical markers for this analysis of Medieval Britain. Out of the turbulence came stronger senses of identity in Scotland, Wales, and Ireland. Yet this was an age, too, of growing definition of Englishness and of a distinctive English cultural tradition.

The Tudors John Guy

The most authoritative short introduction to this exciting long century, *The Tudors* offers a compelling account of the political, religious, and economic changes in Britain under such leading monarchs as Henry VIII and Elizabeth I. This Very Short Introduction also provides a comprehensive reassessment of the reigns of Henry VII, Edward VI, and Philip and Mary.

Stuart Britain John Morrill

A century of revolution is here set into its political, religious, social, economic, intellectual, and cultural contexts. This title describes the effects of a period during which population was growing inexorably, faster than both the food supply and the employment market. Morrill also portrays the unexpected irruption into civil war which then took on a terrifying momentum of its own, resulting in violent revolution and in the abolition of the monarchy, the House of Lords, and the established Church. He goes on to describe how painfully and with what difficulty order and obedience were restored.

THE
World turn'd upside down:
OR,
A briefe description of the ridiculous Fashions of these distracted Times.

By T.J. a well-willer to King, Parliament and Kingdom.

London : Printed for *John Smith.* 1647.

7. **The World Turn'd Upside Down: inversions of gender, society, and the body were linked to the political troubles of 17th-century England.**

Eighteenth-Century Britain   **Paul Langford**

Eighteenth-century Britain is sometimes thought of as sedate, oligarchical, and conservative. Langford reveals the essential vitality as Britain evolved into a great power, an industrial giant, and a dynamic commercial society. The transforming effect of 100 years is concisely narrated in all its diversity and complexity.

Nineteenth-Century Britain   **Christopher Harvie and H. C. G. Matthew**

A sharp but subtle account of remarkable economic and social change – and an even more remarkable political stability. Britain in 1789 was overwhelmingly rural, agrarian, multilingual, and almost half Celtic. By 1914, when it faced its greatest test since the defeat of Napoleon, it was largely urban and English. The authors highlight the forces behind Britain's rise to its imperial zenith, and the continuing tensions within the nations of the 'union state'.

Twentieth-Century Britain   **Kenneth O. Morgan**

The forces of consensus and of conflict in 20th-century Britain are discussed in this wide-ranging yet concise analysis of the last century. Morgan covers the trauma of the First World War and the social divisions of the 1920s; fierce domestic and foreign policy debates in the 1930s; the impact of the Second World War on domestic transformation, popular culture, and the loss of empire; the transition from the turmoil of the 1970s to the aftermath of Thatcherism and the advent of New Labour. Profound tensions that shook the United Kingdom are juxtaposed against an equally deep desire for stability, cohesion, and a sense of historic identity.

Empire   **Stephen Howe**

A great deal of the world's history is the history of empires. Howe explores the idea of empire in the widest sense, from the ancient Roman Empire, through the colonization of the Americas and the Soviet empire, to our recent memories of colonial rule and the new economic-based imperial systems. This is a challenging and compelling book that offers new insights into profound changes in the modern world.

Writers on empire

The conquest of the earth, which mostly means the taking it away from those who have a different complexion or slightly flatter noses than ourselves, is not a pretty thing when you look at it too much. What redeems it is the idea only. An idea at the back of it; not a sentimental pretence but an idea; an unselfish belief in the idea – something you can set up, and bow down before, and offer a sacrifice to.

Joseph Conrad in *Heart of Darkness* (1899)

And it was at this moment, as I stood there with the rifle in my hands, that I first grasped the hollowness, the futility of the white man's dominion in the East. Here was I, the white man with his gun, standing in front of the unarmed native crowd – seemingly the leading actor in the piece; but in reality I was only an absurd puppet pushed to and fro by the will of those yellow faces behind. I perceived in this moment that when the white man turns tyrant it is his own freedom that he destroys. He becomes a sort of hollow, posturing dummy, the conventionalized figure of a sahib. For it is a condition of his rule, that he shall spend his life in trying to impress the 'natives' and so in every crisis he has got to do what the 'natives' expect of him. He wears a mask, and his face grows to fit it.

George Orwell in 'Shooting an Elephant' (1936)

8. **Imperialists:** The Emperor Timur receiving his grandson Pir Muhammad. The former 'barbarian' conqueror now rules peacefully amidst all the trappings of Islamic imperial high culture – and has time for the family.

The French Revolution   **William Doyle**

Every person of good general knowledge in the 19th century knew something about the great upheaval that had marked the last years of the 18th. Nobody who knew anything of France, even at second hand (if only through learning what was still the first foreign language of choice throughout most of the world), could fail to imbibe some sense that this country had been marked by a traumatic convulsion only just beyond living memory. Many believed, or felt, that this must have been for the best and somehow necessary. New nations have been proud to proclaim their emancipation, or to anticipate it, like the patriots of Brussels in 1789, or Milan in 1796, by adopting tricolour flags. This banner of liberty still flies from Rome to Mexico City, from Bucharest to Dublin. Poles, who first sang the *Marseillaise* in 1794 as they resisted the carve-up of their country, sang it again in 1956 in revolt against Soviet tyranny. In 1989, as France commemorated the Revolution's 200th anniversary, the same anthem of defiance was heard in Beijing, among the doomed student protesters in Tiananmen Square. Few countries have failed to experience some sort of revolution since 1789, and in all of them there have been people looking back to what happened in France then and subsequently for inspiration, models, patterns, or warnings.

> *'The best introduction to its subject in any language'*
> Tim Blanning, University of Cambridge

The Russian Revolution   **S. A. Smith**

The years between 1918 and 1922 in Russia witnessed a level of strife and anarchy unparalleled since the 'Time of Troubles' of 1605–13, when struggles between pretenders to the throne brought Russia to a state of chaos. The civil war brutalized social life to an unimaginable degree, yet as an epic struggle between the new and old worlds it inspired idealism and heroism among the dedicated minorities who supported the Red and White causes. The young Bolshevik V. Poliansky recalled:

> We all lived in an atmosphere of revolutionary romanticism, tired, exhausted, but joyful, festive, our hair uncut, unwashed, unshaven, but bright and clear in heart and mind.

Yet the reality was that Russia succumbed to an economic and social cataclysm. The population on Soviet territory fell by 12.7 million between 1917 and early 1922, only partly due to civil war as such. The losses of Soviet armed forces ranged from 1,150,000 to 1,250,000; and, when the losses of Whites, partisans, and nationalist forces are included, war-related losses rise to between 2.5 million and 3.3 million. Far more perished as a result of disease – between 1917 and 1920 over 2 million died of typhus, typhoid fever, smallpox, and dysentery – causing Lenin to warn that, 'either the louse will defeat socialism or socialism will defeat the louse'. Finally, and most hideously, between 1921 and 1922 as many as 6 million died of starvation and disease in a famine that devastated the Volga region and Ukraine. Not without reason did the novelist Boris Pasternak conclude: 'In our days even the air smells of death.'

The First World War **Michael Howard**

This book is no more than it claims: a very short introduction to a very big subject. But to provide this in 35,000 words for something so vast, complex, and controversial is quite an achievement. To explain why the assassination of an Austrian archduke in an obscure province of the Habsburg Empire caused a conflagration that resulted in some 13 million deaths, the fall of four great dynasties, revolution everywhere east of the Rhine, and the near collapse of the global economy demands the thousands of volumes that historians began to write long before the war came to an end. The more of them one reads, the more bewildered one is likely to get.

If there was a single political cause for the war, it was the advent among the European powers of a dynamic new German Empire whose combination of military, economic, and industrial strength seemed, to its ruling classes, to entitle it to a ranking among world powers that it did not as yet possess. At the same time it appeared threatened by a domestic instability that made its rulers apprehensive as well as ambitious. Simultaneously, the growth of nationalism among the Slav peoples of Central and Southeast Europe threatened the survival of Germany's ally, the multi-national Habsburg Empire. In both countries war increasingly seemed the only solution to their problems, but this mood was general not only in Vienna and Berlin. Throughout Europe there was a sense that war would be a necessary therapy for a society that urbanization, secularization, and modernization were making degenerate and decadent. Rupert Brooke was not the only poet who felt like 'a swimmer into cleanness leaping' when Britain declared war on 14th August 1914.

Those primarily concerned with planning the war knew that unless it could be rapidly won its consequences would be terrible. They hoped that, like its predecessors of 1866 and 1870, it could be settled in a few great battles, leaving the framework of society undisturbed. There were indeed great battles, notably those of Tannenberg and the Marne, but they settled nothing. Belligerent governments summoned up reserves of man-power, converted their industries to the production of munitions, found financial resources from loans, taxes, or simply inflation, and settled down to a war of attrition. This involved wearing down not only each other's armies but their entire societies to the point of collapse; killing their soldiers and starving their civilians. The greater the sacrifices they suffered, the more reluctant they were to consider any peace short of total victory.

For the Germans this was understandable. By the end of 1917 they had beaten the Russians out of the war, and repelled French and British attacks on their Western Front, inflicting on their opponents almost unendurable losses. Those losses, and the appalling conditions in which they were suffered, are now almost all that is remembered in Britain about the war, which makes it all the more desirable to have a short book such as this one to set them in some kind of context. But in spite of their losses, the Allies were unlikely to collapse so long as they were sustained by the resources of a neutral but friendly United States, potentially the most powerful nation in the world. But those resources could be denied them, so the German Navy argued, by unrestricted submarine attacks that took no account of the nationality of the ships they sank. To use these measures would almost certainly bring America into the war, but it seemed a risk worth taking: by the time that country had raised, trained, and transported an effective army, the war would have been won.

It very nearly was. The decision for unrestricted submarine warfare was taken in December 1916, and the United States declared war the following April. It did take a year to transport the first of its forces to Europe. By then Russia had collapsed. German armies had occupied its western provinces from the Black Sea to the Baltic, and had begun organizing them as an impregnable fortress – the Greater German Reich that Hitler was to create 25 years later. The Germans were now free to launch a series of attacks in the West to destroy the French and British armies before the Americans could arrive. They very nearly succeeded. But it was their last throw. The Allies not only held on, but were able to counter-attack; and by the summer the Americans were there to help them.

The German armies in France withdrew in good order, but the knowledge of American forces still to come, as much as the effect of those already there, totally demoralized the High Command – as did the imminence of revolution at home. They opened negotiations for an armistice, but the Allies would grant nothing but a diktat, which they were in no position to reject. The imperial government was overthrown on 9th November, and the bewildered representatives of the new regime found themselves signing an armistice that was a virtual act of surrender on 11th November.

The peace that followed was no real settlement, and everyone knew it. The redrawing of Central and Eastern European frontiers along the lines of nationality has stood the test of time, but Germany remained the strongest power in Europe and irreconciled to her humiliation. The alliance that had defeated Germany disintegrated, leaving only an exhausted France to counterbalance that power on the continent. An equally exhausted Britain, attention fixed on its restive empire, tried belatedly to appease the Germans. But by then a leader had arisen who promised to restore German dignity and power, which he did, and a great deal more besides.

Arguably, the First World War was only the first phase of a Thirty Years' War. But that is another story.

> *'succinct, comprehensive and beautifully written'*
> Times Literary Supplement

Fascism   **Kevin Passmore**

What are the prospects for fascism today? So far no movement that openly assumes the mantle of historic fascism has come close to making a political breakthrough. The explanation for this failure is not only that for most people fascism evokes fear, but that many of the features of inter-war society which made fascism what it was – for example, the medical profession's belief in eugenics, the conviction that national security depended on a high birth rate among the 'native' population and economic autarky, and young men's predilection for uniforms and marching – are no longer so evident in contemporary society. This book unravels the paradoxes of one of the most important phenomena of the modern world, tracing its early origins and its more recent manifestations internationally, and concluding with a look at the extreme right in Europe today.

Nazi Germany: The Enabling Act 1933

The opening session of the last Reichstag took place in the Kroll Opera House, situated on the Tiergarten in central Berlin, for the Reichstag building had been destroyed by fire a few weeks previously. Inside the hall a huge swastika flag hung behind the platform occupied by the cabinet and President of the Reichstag. Only one item lay before the Reichstag: an Enabling Law, giving the Chancellor the power to issue laws without the approval of the Reichstag, even where they deviated from the constitution. Frowning intensely, Hitler read his declaration with an unusual self-possession. In reply, the socialist Otto Wels courageously invoked the 'principles of humanity and justice, of freedom and socialism'. Yet the French Ambassador remembered that he spoke with the air of a beaten child. His voice choking with emotion, Wels concluded by expressing best wishes to those already filling concentration camps and prisons. Hitler responded by accusing socialists of having persecuted the Nazis for 14 years. Socialists heckled, but stormtroopers behind them hissed 'you'll be strung up today'.

The Enabling Law was passed by 444 votes against the 94 of the socialists. It destroyed the rule of law and in practice licensed the Nazis to act as they saw fit, in the 'higher interests of the German people', against anyone deemed to be an enemy of the Reich.

> *'excellent introduction ... concise and refreshingly free of jargon.'*
>
> Times Literary Supplement

9. 'We're voting for Hitler'. Poster from the 1932 presidential election campaign.

The Cold War   **Robert McMahon**

The vast swath of death and destruction precipitated by the Second World War left not only much of Europe and Asia in ruins but the old international order as well. 'The whole world structure and order that we had inherited from the nineteenth century was gone', marvelled US Assistant Secretary of State Dean Acheson. Indeed, the Eurocentric international system that had dominated world affairs for the past 500 years had, virtually overnight, vanished. Two continent-sized military behemoths – already being dubbed superpowers – had risen in its stead, each intent upon forging a new order consonant with its particular needs and values. As the war moved into its final phase, even the most casual observer of world politics could see that the United States and the Soviet Union held most of the military, economic, and diplomatic cards. On one basic goal, those adversaries-turned-allies were in essential accord: that some semblance of authority and stability needed to be restored with dispatch – and not just to those areas directly affected by the war but to the broader international system as well. The task was as urgent as it was daunting since, as Under Secretary of State Joseph Grew warned in June 1945: 'Anarchy may result from the present economic distress and political unrest.'

Modern Ireland   **Senia Pašeta**

The Act of Union between Great Britain and Ireland which came into effect on 1 January 1801 presents historians with a convenient but far from straightforward starting point for a survey of modern Irish history. Many of the conflicts which have characterized Irish political, social, and economic life since 1800 were in place well before the Act was introduced. International events were already exacerbating local tensions. The violent and dynamic final three decades of the 18th century which prompted the introduction of the Act were themselves products of a longer and constantly evolving struggle between competing political minds, identities, and programmes. The Act of Union attempted to address the issues underlying the conflicts, but each one continued to simmer throughout the next two centuries.

Northern Ireland   **Marc Mulholland**

Bloody Sunday, on 30th January 1972, was the debacle that led to the almost complete collapse of Catholic opposition to political violence. Confronting a relatively small-scale riot, the elite parachute regiment shot dead 13 unarmed demonstrators (a 14th died later of wounds). One British Army officer indicated perfectly the self-defeating militarism of counter-insurgency: 'When we moved on the streets we moved as if we in fact were moving against a well-armed, well-trained army.' Not one of the fatalities on Bloody Sunday was an IRA man. Had the British Army fired on a similar crowd a month later, again targeting men of military age, they would hardly have been able to avoid enemy kills: Bloody Sunday led to a mass influx into the ranks of the Derry IRA. The relentless bombing campaign was accelerated; of the city's 150 shops, only 20 were left trading. Almost one-third of the 320 deaths in Derry attributed to the Troubles were the result of street clashes and gun battles during this period (54 of those killed were members of the Security Forces).

Terrorism   **Charles Townshend**

Terrorism upsets people. It does so deliberately. That is its point, and that is why it has engaged so much of our attention at the turn of the 21st century. The 11th September 2001 attack on New York saw damage that looked like a wartime air raid. Although the casualty list mercifully shrank from a potential 50,000 to 5,000, and finally to less than 4,000, the vision of mass destruction, previously restricted to the kind of weapons possessed by only a handful of major powers, had appeared.

The search for an 'adequate' definition of terrorism is still on. Why the difficulty? In a word, it is 'labelling', because 'terrorist' is a description that has almost never been voluntarily adopted by any individual or group, possibly as a result of the notion that one person's terrorist is another's freedom fighter. It is applied to them by others, first and foremost by the governments of the states they attack. Terrorism appears to be a state of mind rather than an activity.

What is terrorism?

'The calculated use or threat of violence to inculcate fear, intended to coerce or intimidate governments or societies.'

US Government

'The use or threat, for the purpose of advancing a political, religious or ideological course of action, of serious violence against any person or property.'

UK Government

'Terrorism is a distinctive form of modern political agency, intended to threaten the ability of a state to ensure the security of its members.'

Sunil Khilnani, Professor of Politics, UCL

Killing

How can terrorists go out and kill innocent people in cold blood? A typical example is the assertion that terrorists need to be 'without the human emotions of pity or remorse'. This suggestion of monstrosity results from a false antinomy between 'cold blood' and 'the heat of battle' – the latter being what supposedly makes it possible for ordinary people to kill in war. This kind of distinction, together with the notion of the 'enemy' as being a collective group rather than individuals, has powered most, if not all, of the wars, genocides, and violent revolutionary struggles in the modern world, and remains the common currency of nationalist discourse and the motor of ethnic cleansing.

'Like the other excellent books in this series, this is rigorous and compelling . . . balanced, sensible.'

Independent on Sunday

Democracy   **Bernard Crick**

No political concept is more used and misused than that of democracy. Here, Crick examines the history of the doctrine, practices, and institutions of democracy. There are many meanings attached to the word 'democracy'; it is what philosophers have called 'an essentially contested concept' because the very definition carries a different social, moral, or political agenda. Plato detested the concept of democracy, considering it to be the rule of opinion over knowledge. Whereas for his pupil, Aristotle, democracy was a basic condition for good government.

Politics   **Kenneth Minogue**

This provocative yet balanced view of politics prompts us to consider why political systems evolve, how politics offers both power and order in our society, whether democracy is a good thing, and the future of politics in the 21st century.

Politics is so central to our civilization that its meaning changes with every change of culture and circumstance. For this reason, our first move in trying to understand politics must be to free ourselves from the unreflective beliefs of the present. One aim of this book is to explain how it came about that what used to be a limited activity conducted by the elites of some Western countries is now thought to be the inescapable preoccupation of mankind. Why do we need politics? If men were angels, no government would be needed. But

since some sort of government *is* needed, could we not find a
better solution than the states revealed to us by history as riddled
with war, poverty, and violence? High hopes of this kind have
often erupted among the poor on the margins of politics, and
have sometimes captured the centre. Such hopes unmistakably
derive from a millennial version of Christianity, and they have had
explosive consequences.

British Politics   **Tony Wright**

Try this game. You have to fill in the blank.

French wine
Italian food
German cars
British __

Not easy, is it? One suggestion might be 'language', which would be
the obvious candidate except for the fact that it is not *English* but
British that we are talking about (a characteristic confusion that is
discussed in this book). This also disqualifies 'hooligans'.

There is a good case to be made for 'politics' or 'government'. This is
not an original answer. Indeed, it has long been held (not least by
the British) that Britain has displayed a particular approach to
politics that has offered lessons to the world in making government
work. 'This country's distinctive contribution to civilisation',
proclaimed the *Daily Telegraph* not so long ago, 'has been the
development of stable institutions of representative government.'
There is plenty to unpick in such a statement (which country
precisely?; what kind of stability?; does representative mean
democratic?), but it faithfully echoes a long line of such judgements
about the political genius and blessings of the British.

The European Union   **John Pinder**

The European Union of today is the result of a process that began half a century ago with the creation of the European Coal and Steel Community. Those two industries then provided the industrial muscle for military power; and Robert Schuman, the French Foreign Minister, affirmed on 9th May 1950, in his declaration to launch the project, that 'any war between France and Germany' would become 'not merely unthinkable, but materially impossible'. The Union has the capacity to provide the framework for Europe's new economy and democratic stability, and to assist the development of a world system that can deliver security and sustainable development.

It may not be easy, at today's distance, to appreciate how much this meant, only five years after the end of the war of 1939–45 which had brought such terrible suffering to almost all European countries. For France and Germany, which had been at war with each other three times in the preceding eight decades, finding a way to live together in a durable peace was a fundamental political priority that the new Community was designed to serve. John Pinder shows us how and why the Union was set up, and how it has developed.

'Invaluable'   The Observer

Machiavelli   **Quentin Skinner**

Machiavelli died nearly 500 years ago, but his name lives on as a byword for cunning, duplicity, and the exercise of bad faith in political affairs. Machiavelli's criticism of classical and contemporary humanism is a simple but devastating one. He argues that, if a ruler wishes to reach his highest goals, he will not always find it rational to be moral; on the contrary, he will find that any consistent attempt to cultivate the princely virtues will prove to be a ruinously irrational policy. But what of the Christian objection that this is a foolish as well as a wicked position to adopt, since it forgets the Day of Judgement on which all injustices will finally be punished? About this Machiavelli says nothing at all. His silence is eloquent, indeed epoch-making; it echoed around Christian Europe, at first eliciting a stunned silence in return, and then a howl of execration that has never finally died away.

> *'an informative study.'* The Daily Telegraph

Gandhi   **Bhikhu Parekh**

Deeply unhappy with the basic thrust of modern civilization, Gandhi spent most of his adult life exploring an alternative. In Western thought such exploration has generally taken the form of constructing a Utopian, or ideal, society. Gandhi believed that, since different societies had different histories and traditions, the search for a single model was both incoherent and dangerous. For him, all that a critic could and should do was to suggest the general principles that should govern the good society, leaving each society free to realize them in its own unique way. Gandhi's regulative principles of the good society were derived from his theory of human nature. The good society should be informed by the spirit of cosmic piety. Since human beings are not masters or owners, but guardians, of the rest of creation, they should so organize their collective life that it respects the latter's integrity, diversity, rhythm, and inner balance, and make no greater demands on it than are required for a life of moderate comfort.

Forthcoming
African History, John Parker and Richard Rathbone
Mandela, Tom Lodge

Chapter 5
Heaven and Hell

Introduction **by Damien Keown**

In today's 'global village' understanding one's own religion or culture is no longer enough: we need in addition to understand how and why our neighbour may see things differently. The series of Very Short Introductions includes many titles that illustrate how the enduring and deeply influential phenomenon of religious belief has influenced the major cultures and civilizations of the world.

The series includes volumes on Buddhism, Hinduism, Islam, and Judaism – with a forthcoming volume on Christianity shortly to complete the set of five main world religions. There are further titles on some of the founders and significant historical figures of these religions, such as the Buddha and Saint Paul. Two Very Short Introductions introduce important religious scriptures – the Bible and the Koran – and another explores the broad subject of theology. This is a measure of the interest in the subject of religion in today's multicultural world.

Much of the most exciting contemporary work in theology and ethics is being produced at the interface of different religious traditions, where discussion generates insights and creative resolution of global problems. On issues such as human rights, poverty, the environment, and scientific developments in genetics, there is a surprising amount of convergence among religions. In the interfaith discussions I have attended, it has always seemed clear that there is much more that unites than divides the different religious traditions, an intuition that can be confirmed by browsing through the titles on religion in the VSI series.

But is it possible to condense such a vast topic as a religion – with its complex doctrines and often thousands of years of history – into a single volume, and a slim one at that? When asked to contribute to the series myself, I was sceptical that this could be done, but I am now a confirmed believer in the 'small is beautiful' approach to introductions. Requiring authors to focus only on the essentials produces a clearer and sharper picture. Once the key concepts have been grasped, longer supplementary works can be consulted as required, but the task of learning is greatly enhanced by a good primer.

Clearly, no short work can be exhaustive, but a surprising amount of information can be compressed into a small number of pages, especially by making skilful and appropriate use of text boxes, diagrams, maps, and chronologies, as the series manages to do. As an example, my own volume on Buddhism includes chapters discussing the nature and definition of Buddhism, the life of the Buddha, karma and cosmology, Buddhist doctrine, Mahayana Buddhism, Buddhist ethics, and Buddhism in the West. For the past few years I have used this volume as a set text for my undergraduate classes on Buddhism, with considerable success. Other authors in the series classify their subject in different ways, but each volume on the world religions provides the essential information required to understand the main teachings, beliefs, and historical evolution of that tradition and its place in the modern world.

It is precisely the challenges of modernity that will lead many readers, perplexed at contemporary events, to peruse these volumes in order to understand the motives of those who act in ways that otherwise seem incomprehensible. The tragic events of 11th September 2001 in New York, so graphically witnessed on television, continue to reverberate at a global level in social, political, and economic circles. Following these events, Americans have been reading introductory works on Islam at an unprecedented rate in an attempt to comprehend those who could strike at their country with such hatred. And it is not only Americans who are seeking to understand Islam – as the recent bombings in Bali and Kenya have demonstrated, Islamic fundamentalism is a global force that affects not just the United States. In this connection, the volume on Islam in this series, together with the forthcoming one on fundamentalism, will provide an excellent starting point for anyone seeking to comprehend the motives of groups like al-Qaida, and the relationship between political objectives, violence, and religious faith.

Many in the West, of course, have turned away from religion in favour of 'modernity', only to find the secular world, with its individualism and consumer values, spiritually unfulfilling. Writers such as Charles Taylor have described how the search for 'a momentary sense of wow!' has displaced religious life, leading to a feeling of drift, lack of practical conviction, and loss of meaning. Related to this is the phenomenon of religious consumerism – church and faith shopping – whereby religions are mixed and matched as required. Think of Madonna's mystical odyssey through Kabbalah, yoga, and Buddhism, or Bob Dylan's spiritual saga involving encounters with Christianity, Judaism, and atheism.

Although the phenomenon of declining church attendance is often adduced as an indicator of the progressive secularization of Western society (on average only some 20% of Europeans describe themselves as actively involved in religious practice), readers seem to have a greater appetite than ever for books about religion. In part this paradox may be explained by the fact that the 'West' is not a homogeneous entity: in a June 1998 CNN/USA Today Gallup poll, 62% of Americans said that religion is 'very important' in their own lives, 70% claimed to be members of a church or synagogue, and 40% said they had attended religious services the previous week.

One thing is for sure: religious pluralism is an essential feature of the modern world and is likely to remain so. The United States, apart from being the only remaining superpower, is now the most religiously diverse nation on earth. In a world where denominational loyalties are often entwined with racial, ethnic, or national identities, and where religious faith is often used (or misused) in the quest for political and military objectives, a sound understanding of the world's diverse faiths can go a long way to secure peace and harmony among nations.

Theology   **David F. Ford**

David Ford provides both believers and non-believers with a balanced survey of the central questions of contemporary theology. He inspects the principles underlying religious belief, including the centrality of salvation to most major religions, the changing concept of God over time, and the issue of sin and evil. He also probes the nature of experience, knowledge, and wisdom in theology, and discusses what is involved in interpreting theological texts today.

What about Jesus?

Considering Jesus theologically means neither taking the Jesus of mainstream Christian worship as the last word, nor being continually blown about by fashions. It is rather about pursuing, in ways that take seriously the best available scholarship and theological thinking, basic questions such as: How is the New Testament and other testimony to Jesus to be understood and assessed? What is to be made of the classic developments in Christian doctrine about Jesus, which lie behind the ways in which he is related to in contemporary Christian faith? What is the significance of the amazing variety of images and portrayals of Jesus through history and the world today?

'it succeeds brilliantly in its task of introduction.'
Stephen Sykes, Bishop of Ely

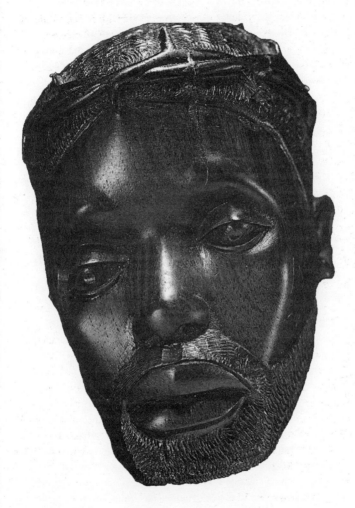

10. Christ with the crown of thorns, depicted in a 20th-century wood carving.

The Bible   **John Riches**

The Bible is one of the most influential and widely read books in the world, selling 2.5 billion copies between 1815 and 1975, and translated into over 350 different languages. Here, the author looks at the importance accorded to the Bible by different communities and cultures and attempts to explain why it has generated such a rich variety of uses and interpretations.

Rogue editions of the Bible

Printers' errors and unusual translations have led to a number of versions of the Bible gaining nicknames. These are some of the better known:

Printers' Bible: with 'Printers' for 'Princes' in Psalm 119:161, producing, for the publishers, the finely appropriate sentence: 'Printers have persecuted me without a cause.'

Vinegar Bible: 1717 edition with a running title for Luke 22 reading 'the parable of the vinegar', for 'vineyard'.

Wicked Bible: 1632 edition in which the seventh commandment reads: 'Thou shalt commit adultery.'

'offers a balanced, scholarly overview.'   The Independent

The Koran   **Michael Cook**

The Koran has constituted a remarkably resilient core of identity and continuity for a religious tradition that is now in its 50th century. Today, there are significant Muslim populations of diverse ethnic origins in all major Western countries. The total number of Muslims in the world is somewhat over a billion, comprising almost one-fifth of the world's population. To help the reader understand this important religion, Michael Cook provides a lucid and direct account of the significance of the Koran both in the modern world and in that of traditional Islam.

Each of the major Eurasian traditions that dominate the history of literate culture has possessed some body of authoritative texts, the transmission of which has been central to its continuing identity. The Greeks had their Homer, the Jews and Christians their Bible, the Zoroastrians their Avesta, the Hindus their Vedas, and the Muslims their Koran. In terms of character and content, these texts do not have much in common. What they share is their centrality to their respective cultures.

> *'informative, witty, and rich with insight. The author firmly places the Koran within its broader context, lending his treatment depth and vigour.'*
>
> Mohamed Mahmoud, Tufts University

Islam   **Malise Ruthven**

This extremely readable book contains essential insights into issues such as why there are major divisions between different Islamic movements – the Shi'ites, the Sunnis, and the Wahhabis – and the central importance of the sharia (Islamic law) in Islamic life. It also offers fresh perspectives on contemporary questions, such as why the greatest 'Jihad' (holy war) is now specifically against the enemies of Islam, rather than the struggle against evil.

The purpose of Islam

The word Islam means in Arabic 'self-surrender'; it is closely related etymologically to *salaam*, the word for peace. The universal greeting with which Muslims address one other, and foreigners, is *as salaam 'alaikum* – peace be upon you.

If there is a single word that can be taken to represent the primary impulse of Islam, be it theological, political, or sociological, it is *tawhid* – making one, unicity. Although the word does not occur in the Koran, the concept it articulates is implicit in the credal formula *there is no god but God*, and there are references to the God who is without partners or associates throughout the holy text. The absolute insistence that it is unicity above all that defines divinity appears in striking, if ironic, contrast with the disunity observable in the Muslim world. It is as if the aspiration to realize divine unicity in terms of the social and political order is forever destined to wreck itself on the shores of human perversity.

Muhammad as model

Muhammad's role as a source of emulation is far from being confined to mystics and visionaries. The physical details of his life – the cut of his beard, the clothes he wore, the food he was reported to have liked – came to be seen as models of human comportment and human behaviour. Honey and mutton were cherished because he cherished them; dogs were considered unclean because – according to a well-known legend – 'the angels do not enter a house in which there is a dog or statues'. The medieval mind saw in Muhammad's every activity the perfection of conduct, in his every opinion a direct guidance from God.

'excellent.'   The Guardian

Judaism   Norman Solomon

Discussing Judaism as a living religion, in all its contemporary richness and variety, the author provides a perceptive and often humorous introduction to the central features and characters of Judaism, from its spiritual leaders, poets, and philosophers, to its eccentrics, including the mystic who tried to convert the pope and the Berber princess who held up the Arab invasion of Spain. The emphasis lies with the *creative* history of Judaism. The suffering and the persecutions and the forced migrations cannot be denied, but amazingly throughout the centuries the spirit has flourished with a still unending procession of poets and saints, of philosophers and of Bible commentators, of grammarians and talmudists, of lawyers and satirists and pastors, of unsung women and men of humble faith.

> *'Norman Solomon has achieved the near impossible with his enlightened book . . . a small masterpiece.'*
> Rabbi Julia Neuberger

Buddhism   **Damien Keown**

From its origins in India over 2,000 years ago, Buddhism has spread throughout Asia and is now exerting an increasing influence on Western culture. In clear and straightforward language, the author explains how Buddhism began and how it evolved into its present-day form.

What does Buddhism tell us?

In a very real sense individuals create themselves through their moral choices. By freely and repeatedly choosing certain things, an individual shapes his character, and through his character his future. As the proverb has it: 'Sow an act, reap a habit; sow a habit, reap a character; sow a character, reap a destiny.'

It is desire, in the form of a strong addiction to life and the pleasant experiences that it offers, that causes rebirth. If the five factors of individuality (the physical body, sensations and feelings, cognition, character traits and dispositions, and consciousness or sentiency) are likened to a car, then desire is the fuel that propels it forward.

Improving ourselves

The experiential dimension is of great importance because Buddhism regards the religious life as essentially a course in self-transformation. Spiritual exercises such as meditation generate altered states of consciousness that can accelerate spiritual development. In terms of its importance, meditation may be likened to prayer in Christianity.

> *'impressive'*   Irish Times

Buddha   **Michael Carrithers**

The author guides us through the diverse accounts of the life and teaching of the Buddha. He discusses the social and political background of India in the Buddha's time, and traces the development of his thought. Though the Buddha witnessed his world comprehensively, he was not of it. He was set apart by the high-minded personal morality of the renouncers: 'as a lotus flower is born in water, grows in water, and rises out of water to stand above it unsoiled, so I, born in the world, raised in the world, having overcome the world, live unsoiled by the world'.

> *'a readable and wonderfully lucid introduction to one of mankind's most beautiful, profound, and compelling systems of wisdom. His impressive powers of explanation help us to come to terms with a vital contemporary reality.'*
>
> Bryan Appleyard

Hinduism   **Kim Knott**

Hinduism is practised by 80% of India's population, and by 30 million people outside India. In this Very Short Introduction, Kim Knott combines a succinct and authoritative overview of a major religion with an analysis of the challenges facing it in the future.

11. The Buddha, depicted here in the lotus posture just after he gained enlightenment. He calls upon the earth to witness his achievement by touching it with his right hand. Western Tibet, 11th–12th centuries AD.

In what forms does Hinduism appear in contemporary life?

Hindu gods and goddesses are everywhere in India, hidden within gorgeous temples and small wayside shrines, depicted in intricate stone carvings, looking out benevolently from advertisements. They are featured on calendar prints and film posters, and captured on market stalls and in shop windows, in jewellery and small scriptures. They are woven into the fabric of life in Indian villages and cities, and are now also to be found in Hindu communities from the Caribbean to North America and the UK, from South Africa to Thailand.

'Miracle', 'hallucination', 'simple scientific explanation', 'divine grace', or 'politically inspired hoax' ran the headlines as onlookers sought to explain why, on 22nd September 1995, images of Ganesha the world over were devouring the milk offered to them by their devout followers. The old debate between science and faith was rekindled. Hindus themselves were quietly divided over the phenomenon, but their surprise was not so much at its occurrence as at its scale. Divine manifestations and small miracles are believed to be commonplace in Indian religious life, but that Hindus and their non-Hindu friends around the globe should witness Ganesha's gracious act was extraordinary.

> 'instantly accessible without being in any way condescending or
> an oversimplification . . . issues conveyed with an elegance and
> simplicity'
>
> Julia Leslie, SOAS, London

Paul   E. P. Sanders

Paul is the most powerful human personality in the history of the Church. A missionary, theologian, and religious genius, he laid down in his epistles the foundations on which later Christian theology was built. In this highly original introduction to Paul's life and thought, the author pays equal attention to Paul's fundamental convictions and the sometimes convoluted ways in which they worked out.

Why is Paul so important to us today?

He forces us, in fact, to pose an extremely serious question: must a religion, in addressing diverse problems, offer answers that are completely consistent with one another? Is it not good to have passionate hopes and commitments that cannot all be reduced to a scheme in which they are arranged in a hierarchical relationship?

> 'Sanders makes one think afresh about all sorts of issues . . . read this book.'
>
> Hebrew Christian

Atheism   Julian Baggini

The author provides a positive case for atheism, one which is not simply about rubbishing religious belief, and writes as much about why one should be an atheist as why one should *not* be an atheist.

We human beings often claim that it is our ability to think that distinguishes us from other animals. We are *homo sapiens* – thinking hominids – and our capacity to reason is our distinctive and highest feature. Yet we are not purely rational. It is not just that we are often in the grip of irrational or non-rational forces and desires, it is that our thinking is itself infused with emotion. These feelings shape our thought, often without us realizing it. This book puts forward the rational case for atheism. If we are to make the case for any point of view, the best way to do so is always to appeal to reasons and arguments that can command the widest possible support. Unfortunately, we often approach rational discussions with prejudices, fears, and commitments. Some of these are not founded on reason and that confers on them a certain immunity to the powers of rational argumentation. So it is with atheism, about which few readers will have a neutral outlook.

Forthcoming
Fundamentalism, Malise Ruthven
Christianity, Linda Woodhead

Chapter 6
Expressing ourselves

Introduction   Catherine Belsey

Some people see the arts – painting and sculpture, literature, music, and architecture – as an extra, society's pleasurable reward for carrying out the serious work of science and technology, or manufacturing and sales, come to that. From this point of view, culture gratifies the senses, while science addresses the intellect. But these same people might also concede that the pictures we like, the buildings we feel happy in, and the fiction we choose may tell us something about who we are. Tastes differ, and the differences can be revealing.

The visual arts thrive on controversy these days. Ever since Marcel Duchamp offered a readymade urinal for exhibition in 1917 under the title *Fountain*, artists have apparently vied with each other to outrage the public. Gratifying the senses seems to have gone by the board. Instead, the project looks more like a challenge to the viewer. 'Is it art?', these works seem to ask; 'what is art?'; 'what do we *mean* by art?' In that sense, art poses an intellectual question to the spectator as an individual, and at the same time to society in general. As Cynthia Freeland makes clear in her *Art Theory: A Very Short Introduction*, art has become a conceptual issue, as well as – or instead of? – a pleasure, according to preference.

Tastes vary, and the variations are not always arbitrary or accidental. Monticello, for instance, the house built in the 1770s by Thomas Jefferson, a prominent founder of the American constitution, is elegant, classical, and restrained. It owes its dignity to a direct line of descent from the temples of ancient Greece and Rome, and in the eyes of an observer familiar, however unconsciously, with the authority of this tradition in Western culture, Monticello justifies its understated claim to power. But as Andrew Ballantyne points out in his *Architecture: A Very Short Introduction*, if my ancestors were first-nation Americans who lived on this land without claiming to own it, I might be considerably less impressed by the 'civilized' values of the classical tradition. And if I were descended from the slaves who worked the Monticello plantation, I might well see the same building as symbolizing oppression.

If cultural difference affects our tastes and preferences, does it also play a part in defining who we are? Debates about the influence of violence on television remain unresolved, but most people would probably agree that the characteristics cultures attribute to fictional heroes and villains can tell us a good deal about the values of society. What do 'we' value in our increasingly globalized culture? Courage, evidently, and intelligence, though not necessarily the academic kind. Our fictional detectives and doctors possess an intuitive knowledge and a skill that cannot be taught. Masculinity and

12. **The Parthenon, Athens, Greece** (447–436 BC).

femininity matter, though mercifully that antithesis is gradually becoming less sharply demarcated.

Did the Greeks value the same qualities? On the evidence of their myths and epics, they rated independence; wisdom, to a high degree; and possibly voracious bisexual appetites. And the Romans? Military skill, stoicism, and voracious heterosexual appetites. The difference of other cultures throws into relief the specificity of the values we so easily take for granted in our own.

What makes us the people we are? Since the late 1800s it has come increasingly to seem that we are as much the products of culture as its origin. Most recently poststructuralist theory, in particular, has argued that the ways we think and feel are defined by the meanings we learn. From birth, we are surrounded by a mother tongue that is already in place. Small children learn – and learn to reproduce – the meanings and values inscribed in the language that constitutes their culture. Fortunately, this doesn't make us into robots. We learn a number of cultural dialects – one for the classroom and another for the playground, say – and these jostle for control, or propel us in unexpected directions. But it might help to explain the 'obviousness' of certain values.

In my *Poststructuralism: A Very Short Introduction* I put the case that, because we learn so early that 'democracy', say, is positive and 'dictatorship' wrong, and because many of us learn this before we know much about the details of the political practices the words define, it can seem to go without saying that it would be worth going to war to defend our 'democratic' way of life. Our antagonist, however, might take for granted a quite different set of meanings and values, in which religion was more important than political systems, or revealed truth mattered more than voting. And if poststructuralist theory is right, these values go deep.

No one in their right mind would claim that cultural differences alone cause wars, would they? Probably not: the material and economic issues are at least as important. But if cultures play a significant part in global conflict, cultural issues matter, and the study of culture, and cultures, might be as important as an understanding of science and technology. Some people would even say our survival could depend on it.

Would they have a point? Current theories about culture and the arts are nothing if not controversial. What do *you* think?

Myth   **Robert Segal**

There is no one version of any myth. There are perhaps as many versions of a story as tellings of that story. Theories of myth go back to ancient times. Plato and the Stoics are the best-known ancient theorists, and they offer contrary approaches to myth. Modern theories hail from long-standing disciplines such as philosophy, religious studies, and literature, but modern theories come most effusively from the social sciences – anthropology, sociology, and psychology. Most disciplines harbour multiple theories. To study myth is to apply to it one or more theories from one or more disciplines.

Literary Theory   **Jonathan Culler**

What is literature? If a five-year-old is asking, it's easy. 'Literature', you answer, 'is stories, poems, plays.' But if the questioner is a literary theorist, it's harder to know how to take the query. 'What is literature?' asks not for a definition but for an analysis, even an argument, about why one might concern oneself with literature at all.

How can we define literature?

Are there any essential, distinguishing features that literary works share? Works of literature come in all shapes and sizes, and most of

Anthony Haden-Guest

13 'You're a terrorist? Thank God. I understood Meg to say you were a theorist.'

them seem to have more in common with works that aren't usually called literature than with some other works recognized as literature. Charlotte Brontë's *Jane Eyre*, for instance, more closely resembles an autobiography than it does a sonnet, and a poem by Robert Burns – 'My love is like a red, red rose' – resembles a folk-song more than it does Shakespeare's *Hamlet*. Are there qualities shared by poems, plays, and novels that distinguish them from, say, songs, transcripts of conversations, and autobiographies?

> *'It is impossible to imagine a clearer treatment of the subject, or one that is, within the given limits of length, more comprehensive.'*
>
> Sir Frank Kermode

Postmodernism   **Christopher Butler**

Christopher Butler considers postmodernist artists, intellectual gurus, academic critics, philosophers, and social scientists as if they were all members of a loosely constituted and quarrelsome political party. This party is by and large internationalist and 'progressive'. It is on the left rather than the right, and it tends to see everything, from abstract painting to personal relationships, as political undertakings. It is not particularly unified in doctrine, and even those who have most significantly contributed ideas to its manifestos sometimes indignantly deny membership – and yet the postmodernist party tends to believe that its time has come. It is certain of its uncertainty, and often claims that it has seen through the sustaining illusions of others, and so has grasped the 'real' nature of the cultural and political institutions which surround us. In doing this postmodernists often follow Marx. They claim to be peculiarly aware of the unique state of contemporary society, immured as it is in what they call 'the postmodern condition'.

The new ideas represented by postmodernism, although they came to inspire some literature, and to dominate its interpretation in academic circles, were actually rooted outside the arts. Of the movement's protagonists, for example, Barthes was mainly interested in the application of linguistic models to the interpretation of text, Derrida's philosophical work began as a critique of linguistics, and Foucault's base was in the social sciences and history. They were also all guided to a greater or lesser degree by the re-reading or redemption of Marx.

> 'a pre-eminently sane, lucid, and concise statement about the central issues, the key examples, and the notorious derelictions of postmodernism.'
>
> Ihab Hassan, University of Wisconsin, Milwaukee

Barthes   Jonathan Culler

Barthes is famous for contradictory reasons. To many, he is above all a theorist, a structuralist, perhaps *the* structuralist, advocate of a systematic, scientific approach to cultural phenomena. To others, Barthes stands for the pleasures of reading and the reader's right to read idiosyncratically. Against a literary criticism focused on authors – interested in recovering what authors thought or meant – Barthes champions the reader and promotes literature that gives the reader an active, creative role.

The theorist as author

Yet this enemy of authors is himself pre-eminently an author, a writer whose varied products reveal a personal style and vision. Many of Barthes' works are idiosyncratic, falling outside established genres: *L'Empire des signes* combines touristic commentary on Japan with a reflection on signs in everyday life and their ethical implications; and *Roland Barthes par Roland Barthes* is a strangely detached account of the life and works of one 'Roland Barthes' that evades the conventions of autobiography.

Poststructuralism   Catherine Belsey

Poststructuralism proposes that the distinctions we make are not necessarily given by the world around us, but are instead produced by the symbolizing systems we learn. How else would we know the difference between pixies and gnomes? But we learn our native tongue at such an early age that it seems transparent, a window on to a world of things, even if some of those things are in practice imaginary, no more than ideas of things, derived from children's stories. Poststructuralists don't (normally) doubt that there is a world: their anxiety concerns what we can claim to know about it with any certainty.

> *'A wonderfully clear account.'*   The Guardian

Postcolonialism   **Robert J. Young**

Postcolonialism describes both an historical condition and a transformation of ways of thinking about the world. Although some former colonies have been 'postcolonial' since the 18th century, 'postcolonialism' is the product of the 20th-century independence movements and the subsequent decolonization of the former empires of Britain, France, Belgium, Holland, Portugal, and the USSR, from 1947 to 1997. Postcolonialism names the political, social, and cultural effects of these historical processes. It also continues the challenge to Western dominance and Western formations of knowledge that constituted the basis of the anti-colonial movements. Although the power relations between empire and colony, centre and margin, have often been reinforced economically since independence, at the same time the identity of 'the West' itself has been subverted through migration, diaspora, and cultural transformation. The politics of postcolonialism began with the deconstruction of ethnocentric assumptions in Western knowledge.

Linguistics   **Peter Matthews**

What would an outsider make of the noises *Homo sapiens* so volubly produces? The words people use are never fixed for all time. *Grotty*, for example, was a new word when it was coined in Britain in the 1960s, and the usage of many speakers of English who were alive at that time has changed to include it. *Gay* in the sense of 'homosexual' seems to have had its origin in prison slang, and in 1950s Britain could still be explained, in a passage cited in *The Oxford English Dictionary*, as 'an American Euphemism'. It has since become familiar, however, even in the speech of many older people who, when they were young, had known it mainly in such phrases as *gay bachelor* or as Wordsworth used it ('A poet cannot but be gay') in his poem about daffodils.

> *'full of facts and figures ... Matthews has carried off a difficult job with real panache. I would recommend this very warmly indeed.'*
>
> Andrew Linn, University of Sheffield

Shakespeare   **Germaine Greer**

The chief pitfall threatening any discussion of Shakespeare's thought is the common assumption that the opinions of any character in a Shakespearian play are Shakespeare's own. Shakespeare was not a propagandist; he did not write plays as vehicles for his own ideas. Rather he developed a theatre of dialectical conflict, in which idea is pitted against idea and from their friction a deeper understanding of the issues emerges. The resolution which is reached is not the negation of the conflict, but the stasis produced by art. Even as we applaud it, we recognize its fragility. It might be said that the strength of Shakespeare's position is that he refrains from coming to conclusions but leaves that to those who complete his utterance, the audience and the actors in the theatre.

Characters and identity

Shakespeare's characters are not defined by their actions, nor are their personalities rigid constructs which control their capacity for action. His personages search for ways to transcend that identity, which is transitory, and free the spirit, which is made in God's likeness, eternal and immutable.

> *'the clearest and simplest explanation of Shakespeare's thought I have yet read'*
>
> Auberon Waugh

Russian Literature   **Catriona Kelly**

The uniqueness of Russian literature (and Russian culture more generally) has been held by many Western observers to lie in precisely its ability to embrace spiritual and material worlds. *Judging* life has been a constant preoccupation of Russian writers, while Pushkin himself is an illustration that intelligent Russians have had just as large a talent for, and inclination towards, *analysis* as their counterparts anywhere in the world. In Russia itself, writers have often been regarded as sages, as moral guides to how life should be lived; but there are many other reasons for reading Russian literature. Like any other literature, it represents the world in new and extraordinary ways, it investigates areas of human experience that we sometimes prefer not to think about (madness, homicidal urges, tyranny); and it offers not only intellectual stimulation but the sensual delight of language stretched to its limits, of laughter, and of flights of imaginative fancy.

'brilliant ... , written with elegance, ... informed, incisive, provocative'

Anthony Cross, University of Cambridge

Art Theory   **Cynthia Freeland**

During a lecture by the prominent environmental artist Robert Irwin, he commented a bit cynically about the vagueness of the term 'art' that it 'has come to mean so many things that it doesn't mean anything any more'. But this didn't stop Irwin from offering his own definition. He proposed to describe art as 'a continuous examination of our perceptual awareness and a continuous expansion of our awareness of the world around us'. This challenging analysis of many centuries of art considers the question: What is art?

Message and meaning

Gender and sexual preference – together with nationality, ethnicity, politics, and religion – all seem to have some impact on the meaning of art. People have debated for centuries about the meaning of some works of art – for example, the *Mona Lisa*'s smile. Does art bear a message in the way language does? What must we know to clarify an artwork's meaning: external facts about artists' lives, or internal facts about how their works were made? Can't we just look at an artwork for enjoyment?

'admirable for its scope, compactness and exceptional clarity. Reader-friendly and thought-provoking'

The Independent

Architecture **Andrew Ballantyne**

We are shaped by the culture that we grow up in, and by the culture in which we participate, whether we think about it or not – and most of the time we don't think about it at all. In architecture, as in any other culture, our sense of 'how things should be' develops from our experience. Each gesture we make means something, but the meaning depends on the culture in which the gesture is understood.

Our experience of architecture

The precise ways in which we respond to buildings vary according to our prior experiences of buildings. Cutting across all considerations of style and taste, we respond also to the kind of life that we suppose to be implied in a building – whether it feels wholesome or dispiriting, sordid or dangerous, whether it opens up new possibilities, or reminds us of places where we have been happy in the past. This is an introduction not just to the way buildings are designed and made, but the way in which we live with them and confer meaning upon them.

'a densely fascinating guide'   The Guardian

Music **Nicholas Cook**

It's an obvious fact that the world is teeming with different kinds of music: traditional, folk, classical, jazz, rock, pop, world, just to name a few. This has always been the case, but modern communications and sound reproduction technology have made musical pluralism part of everyday life. And yet the ways we think about music don't reflect this. Each type of music comes with its own way of thinking about music, as if it were the *only* way of thinking about music (and the only music to think about). In particular, the way of thinking about music that is built into schools and universities – and most books about music, for that matter – reflects the way music was in 19th-century Europe rather than the way it is today, anywhere. The result is a kind of credibility gap between music and how we think about it. In today's world, deciding what music to listen to is a significant part of deciding and announcing to people not just who you want to be . . . but who you *are*.

Technique and interpretation

Between and around the essential note-to-note structure lies a vast domain of interpretive possibility, in which you can choose to play faster or slower, louder or softer, to phrase or articulate one way or another. This is what makes your performance individualistic, drab, eccentric, or just plain brilliant.

> *'a lively and lucid book . . . as a brief guide to the contemporary rethinking of music, it could hardly be bettered.'*
>
> BBC Music

World Music **Philip Bohlman**

At the beginning of the 21st century it is impossible to define world music without slipping down a tautological slope. World music can be folk music, art music, or popular music; its practitioners may be amateur or professional. World music may be sacred, secular, or commercial; its performers may emphasize authenticity, while at

'Ruddy music lessons...'

14. Cartoon by Ronald Searle.

the same time relying heavily on mediation to disseminate it to as many markets as possible. There's ample justification to call just about anything world music. Local musicians become dependent on the global music industry. Traditional melody and functions must undergo transformation in order to be mapped on Western harmony and repackaged for global consumption.

> *'Philip Bohlman's superb study places world music squarely in history – and a lengthy history at that, reaching back to the Age of Discovery and even beyond.'*
> Richard Middleton, University of Newcastle upon Tyne

Forthcoming
Art History, Dana Arnold
Christian Art, Beth Williamson
Dada and Surrealism, David Hopkins
Design, John Heskett
Photography, Steve Edwards

Everything

Chapter 7
Are we all mad?

Introduction   **Dylan Evans**

The human mind faces many challenges in its quest for knowledge, but none greater than the challenge of understanding itself. For many centuries, people did not even know what the mind *was*, let alone how it worked. Most people assumed that the mind was a spiritual substance, quite unlike the material body it inhabited. The eventual recognition that the mind is, in fact, not a spiritual thing – that it is, in fact, not a 'thing' at all, but a process carried out by a purely material organ (the brain) – is probably the most important scientific discovery of all time. But this is just the beginning. We now face the daunting task of discovering *how the mind works*. Since the brain is the most complex object in the known universe, this task is not going to be easy.

It is still early days. Scientific psychology is barely more than 100 years old (see *Psychology: A Very Short Introduction*). Our current knowledge of the mind is probably as rudimentary as our knowledge of physics was in the 17th century, before Newton wrote the *Principia*. Psychology has yet to find its Newton.

Some have laid claim to that title. Sigmund Freud (1856–1939), for example, compared his theory of the unconscious to the revolutionary discoveries of Copernicus and Darwin (see *Freud: A Very Short Introduction*). Similar claims were made by one of Freud's early disciples, Carl Gustav Jung (1875–1961) (see *Jung: A Very Short Introduction*). History has not borne out these claims, however; the ideas of both Freud and Jung have since been superseded by more accurate theories. Our current theories will themselves be superseded as we continue to make progress in discovering how the mind works.

The theory of evolution by natural selection will no doubt play a key role in future developments in psychology. Natural selection has shaped our minds just as it has shaped our bodies, so we should expect our minds to be good at enabling us to do things that help us survive and reproduce. Intelligence, a notoriously difficult concept to define, can perhaps be best understood as the ability to solve adaptive problems (see *Intelligence: A Very Short Introduction*). Emotions play a key role in this ability, and are increasingly seen not as an impediment to intelligent action, but as a vital component of intelligence (see *Emotion: A Very Short Introduction*).

Like all products of evolution, the mind has its fair share of design flaws. It can break down in a number of ways, and the history of our attempts to understand these disorders is a fascinating tale. The most severe disorder is schizophrenia, with its bizarre hallucinations and strange delusions (see *Schizophrenia: A Very Short Introduction*).

Perhaps the greatest challenge of all in understanding the mind will be to understand consciousness. At the dawn of the 21st century, there is still no scientific consensus about what consciousness is. If 99% of what the mind does can be done without consciousness, why not do all of it unconsciously? And what is it that determines which thoughts, of the millions fizzing around our brains, should enter conscious awareness? And why do we have little islands of consciousness in the great ocean of unconsciousness that we call sleep?

Psychology   **Gillian Butler and Freda McManus**

Psychology, as defined by William James, is about the mind or brain, but although psychologists do study the brain, they do not understand enough about its workings to be able to comprehend the part that it plays in the expression of our hopes, fears, and wishes, or in our behaviour during experiences as varied as giving birth or watching a football match. Indeed, it is rarely possible to study the brain directly. So, psychologists have discovered much more by studying our behaviour, and by using their observations to derive hypotheses about what is going on inside us.

Psychology is also about the ways in which organisms, usually people, use their mental abilities, or minds, to operate in the world around them. The ways in which they do this have changed over time as their environment has changed. Evolutionary theory suggests that if organisms do not adapt to a changing environment they will become extinct (hence the sayings 'adapt or die' and 'survival of the fittest'). The mind has been, and is still being, shaped by adaptive processes. This means that there are evolutionary reasons why our minds work the way they do – for instance, the reason we are better at detecting moving objects than stationary ones may be because this ability was useful in helping our ancestors to avoid predators. It is important for psychologists, as well as for those working in other scientific disciplines such as biology and physiology, to be aware of those reasons.

'very readable, stimulating, and well-written'

Anthony Clare

Intelligence   **Ian J. Deary**

The question of how to conceive of human mental capacities is a vexed one. Psychologists have argued about it for most of the 20th century, and the debate continues. The first person to describe the general factor in human intelligence was an English army officer turned psychologist, Charles Spearman, in a famous research paper in 1904. He examined schoolchildren's scores in different academic subjects. The scores were all positively correlated, and he put this down to a general mental ability. There followed decades of arguments among psychologists as to whether or not there was such a single entity.

Indications of intelligence

i) There is a modest association between brain size and psychometric intelligence. People with bigger brains tend to have higher mental test scores. We do not know yet why this association occurs.

ii) People with higher intelligence, on average, appear to elicit faster, more complex, and differently shaped electrical responses when brain activity is recorded by an electroencephalogram (EEG) machine.

iii) There is a well-established, moderate association between the efficiency of the early stages of visual perception and intelligence test scores.

iv) People with higher intelligence test scores have, on average, shorter and less variable reaction times.

'extremely readable ... Without dumbing down or patronising the reader, Ian Deary has done the general public a great service.'
Journal of Nursing

Schizophrenia   **Chris Frith and Eve Johnstone**

Our knowledge of schizophrenia often comes from the popular press. Articles about mental illness are quite frequent, but sufferers and their carers are nearly always portrayed in a negative light. Tabloid papers in particular concentrate on individual cases involving violent death. Sufferers of schizophrenia can become irrational and behave in ways that seem impossible to understand. In fact, the vast majority of sufferers are not dangerous, and if we are to help them we must try to understand them.

What is schizophrenia?

Schizophrenia is the term applied to a severe form of mental disorder, which can be observed in all countries and cultures. At a rough estimate, about 1 person in 100 may experience this disorder at some time in their lives. This life-time risk of 1% is about the same as that for developing rheumatoid arthritis. Many of us will know of someone with this much more visible disorder. The experience of schizophrenia is extremely distressing both for the sufferer and for his or her family and friends. The monetary cost of schizophrenia is also severe. In terms of care and treatment, the annual cost of schizophrenia in the UK in the early 1990s was £397 million, while the indirect costs in terms of lost production were conservatively estimated at the same time to be £1.7 billion.

Drugs   Leslie Iversen

The 20th century saw a remarkable upsurge of research on drugs, with major advances in the treatment of bacterial and viral infections, heart disease, stomach ulcers, cancer, and mental illnesses. These, along with the introduction of the oral contraceptive, have altered all of our lives.

15. New types of drugs, both medicinal and recreational, are being created all the time.

Recreational drugs

The total annual worldwide market for all medical drugs is approximately $250 billion, but the market for recreational drugs is probably at least ten times greater.

Alcohol: the pleasurable intoxicant actions of alcohol seem to be due in part to its ability to stimulate opiate mechanisms in the brain – the same ones that are stimulated more directly and more aggressively by heroin.

Nicotine: acts in the brain on receptors for the chemical messenger acetylcholine. The nerve tracts that release acetylcholine in the brain have among their functions the ability to act as an alerting or arousal system for the cerebral hemispheres – the thinking part of the brain.

Caffeine: one explanation for the stimulant effects of the drug is that by blocking the normal braking actions of adenosine the drug promotes more release of the chemicals acetylcholine and dopamine, both of which have stimulant effects on brain function.

Cannabis: the principal psychoactive ingredient in the plant is the complex chemical delta-9-tetrahydrocannabinol (THC) – there is a specific receptor protein in the brain that recognizes THC (a chemical found only in the cannabis plant).

Amphetamines: one of the first man-made recreational drugs, the military started the first non-medical use of the drug during the Second World War, to keep pilots and other military personnel awake and alert during long missions.

Heroin: in addition to the hazards inherent in the drug itself, users are likely to die from overdose because the street drug is of variable potency and quality. and at high doses the drug depresses respiration.

Cocaine: was incorporated into a number of freely available tonic 'coca-wines', and was an ingredient in the original Coca Colafi, until its dangers were recognized.

'illuminating'　　　　　　　　　　　　　　　　　TNT magazine

Emotion   **Dylan Evans**

Like language, colour, and music, drugs are an ancient form of emotional technology. Alcohol may have been invented as recently as 5,000 or 6,000 years ago, but there is archaeological evidence that humans began using other psychotropic drugs long before this.

16. Love heartfi sweets.

Scientific interest in the emotions underwent something of a renaissance in the 1990s. For much of the 20th century, research in the emotions was confined to a few psychologists and even fewer anthropologists. At the dawn of the 21st century, however, things are rather different. Cognitive psychologists have abandoned their exclusive focus on reasoning, perception, and memory, and are rediscovering the importance of affective processes.

Emotion and A. I.

The most recent discipline to have entered the debate on emotion is artificial intelligence. Since the early 1990s, computer scientists have become increasingly interested in building emotional machines, and workers in robotics are already making some progress in this area. *Emotion: A Very Short Introduction* concludes with a discussion of these recent developments, and speculates on where it will all lead. Will we succeed in building robots that have feelings just like we do? And what might be the consequences of such technology?

'a pop science classic'   Independent on Sunday

Freud   **Anthony Storr**

Sigmund Freud revolutionized the way in which we think about ourselves. From its beginnings as a theory of neurosis, Freud developed psychoanalysis into a general psychology which became widely accepted as the predominant mode of discussing personality and interpersonal relationships.

Freud and dreams

Freud affirmed that, with very few exceptions, dreams were disguised, hallucinatory fulfilments of repressed wishes, often dating from early childhood. This theory is clearly derived from, or comparable with, Freud's early statement about hysteria, in which he supposed that the trauma which provoked the current symptoms did so only because it awoke memories of traumata in childhood. He felt the interpretation of dreams provided a way into the unconscious activities of the mind.

'lucid, fair and astonishingly comprehensive'   Spectator

Jung   **Anthony Stevens**

However fortunate our upbringing may have been, few of us by middle age can hope to be any more than a 'good enough' version of the Self. One can, nevertheless, follow the Apollonian advice to 'know thyself', heed Pindar's dictum 'Become what thou art', and learn from Plato and Aristotle to discover one's 'true self' – to make explicit what implicitly one already is. In Jungian terms this means overcoming the divisions imposed by the parental and cultural milieu, to divest oneself of 'the false wrappings of the persona', and abandon one's ego-defences. It also involves avoiding projecting one's shadow on to others, but striving to know it and acknowledge it as part of one's inner life, and attempting to bring to conscious fulfilment the supreme intentions of the Self. Complete achievement of these objectives within the compass of one individual lifetime is never possible, of course, but that is not the point.

'The goal is important only as an idea,' wrote Jung; 'the essential thing is the *opus* which leads to the goal: *that* is the goal of a lifetime.'

'accessible, authoritative but, above all, very readable'
Clinical Psychology Forum

Dreaming   J. Allan Hobson

Replacing dream mystique with modern dream science, this book provides a new and increasingly complete picture of how dreaming is created by the brain, exploring how this new science is affecting theories in psychoanalysis, and how it is helping our understanding of the causes of mental illness. Dreaming maintains and develops the mind: we go crazy in our dreams in order to avoid doing so when we are awake, and sleep is not just good for health but essential to life.

Do blind people see in their dreams?

People who are blind from birth have no visual imagery at any time, neither in waking nor in dreaming. Vision is not the only modality in visually impaired individuals; bodily sensations or the sense of position of the body in space is markedly enhanced, so these individuals do have other hallucinatory dream experiences.

The brains of people with acquired blindness have developed perceptual capacities. Dreaming is the time in which people with acquired blindness see most clearly.

'engaging new book' The Sunday Telegraph

Everything

Chapter 8
Where are we going?

Introduction
Felipe Fernandez-Armesto

In the 'developed' world today, we agonize over how to identify most of the communities we belong to: we debate the limits of our neighbourhoods, classes, regions, faith-communities, ethnicities, nations, blocs, civilizations. We ask people questions to 'place' them in our panorama of distinctions, or we officiously demand identity-documents to objectify our prejudices. Our sense of species seems, by comparison, obvious. We can spot a fellow human instantly, with no questions asked. We admit the obligations implied by membership of this impressive global community: we are willing to accord what we call human rights to everyone we acknowledge as a fellow member.

Really, though, 'humankind' is a problematic concept: recently invented, unsatisfactorily defined. Most languages have no word for 'human': only a term which designates the group, and another which assimilates outsiders to other ranks – usually those of beasts and demons. The inclusive humanity we take for granted in ourselves is an unusual development, which needs to be traced and explained. And our tendency to congratulate ourselves on it – to praise ourselves for our willingness to embrace all whom we recognize as 'people', of all 'races' and all colours and customs, and of both sexes, in the same category as ourselves – needs to be scrutinized for deficiencies. The story of the broadening of the concept of humankind is not over yet. The question, 'What does it mean to be human?' (or the follow-up question, 'So who is human?')

now evokes among us different answers from those offered in the past or in cultures other than our own, but it remains as difficult to answer as ever.

Potentially inclusive definitions of humanity are traceable in traditions of the first millennium BC in Indian, Greek, and Chinese texts; but all these civilizations – and others with similar concepts – admitted the existence of deficient or humanly imperfect categories within humankind, including women and 'barbarians'. Moreover, they assumed the existence of sub-human species in the interstices of the hierarchy of nature, between those which are fully human and those which are utterly non-human. The problem of where particular beings or groups fitted into this scheme of classification was therefore unresolved. The consequences can be followed in the history of broadening encounters between cultures, especially in the period of earth-girdling navigation, which began in Western Europe about 500 years ago and which provoked challenges to just about everybody's notion of the nature and limits of humankind, as peoples of a previously unanticipated diversity confronted one another for the first time. How could you tell humans from the *similitudines hominis* and monstrous beings who filled the nether links of the chain of being? The question was all the more difficult because some of the postulated categories had a habit of disguising themselves as human, or transgressing the boundaries in puzzling ways: the werewolves, succubi, beast-men, and progeny of bestiality. The story of how these problems were resolved is a long one, characterized at almost every turn by the stunning irrationality of the choices made and the inadequacy of the science invoked to justify them. The ruling principles of what we might call 'humanhood' were vague and provoked more questions: they included possession of reason – but what was reason? – or of a soul – but how do you spot a soul? – or of a body like the observer's – but what differences mattered, and how much?

Landmarks of the story include the Papal Bulls of the 1530s which declared the indigenous peoples of the New World to be fully human, and the continuing debate about the possibility of multiple 'creations' of man in different parts of the world; the discovery by Renaissance anatomists that women were not merely nature's bodged attempts to make men; the long struggle to establish the fully human credentials of blacks and Australian aboriginals; the wrestlings of early-modern intellectuals with the problems posed by anatomical anomalies, such as those of pygmies and Hottentots; and the ever-present debate over the differences between humans and other primates ('degenerate men' in many medieval characterizations).

The last of these debates seemed to have come to an end in the late 18th century, when the scientific world more or less united in rejecting Lord Monboddo's theory that orang-utans were human. By that time, the configurations of humankind were more or less as we now think them to be, with none of the exclusions that had dappled earlier discussions. But the problem was cast back into the crucible by 19th-century developments. Scientific racism multiplied the subcategories into which humankind was split. The new science of social anthropology proposed cultural as well as biological criteria of differentiation. Above all, the theory of evolution made humanhood strictly undefinable: on the one hand, Darwin admitted that blacks and whites might potentially separate into different species; on the other, if men and animals have a common ancestry, where, in the evolution of hominids and the predecessors of such creatures, do we draw the line between those we consider human and those we do not? As Bertrand Russell pointed out, 'a resolute egalitarian will find himself forced to regard apes as the equals of human beings. And why stop with apes? I do not see how he is to resist an argument in favour of Votes for Oysters'. There began two still enduring and still unresolved debates, about the moral implications of our self-definition as humans, and about the problem of how far back in the evolutionary past to distinguish humans from others. We are in a fascinating stage of both debates today. From different perspectives, animal-rights movements and the philosopher John Gray have asked hard questions about what it means to be human in relation to other animals; recent controversies among palaeoanthropologists over the human status of Neanderthals have been conducted in terms startlingly reminiscent of 19th-century debates about blacks. Meanwhile, all kinds of non-biological criteria for humanhood have been proposed (humans are tool-making animals, animals-with-language, cooking animals, animals-with-consciousness, animals-with-imagination, moral animals, and so on) and all, on close scrutiny, prove unsatisfactory.

Still, in the 20th century, humankind had at its disposal the most inclusive self-definition ever: in effect, every group was human if members of other groups could successfully breed with it. Yet, despite this inclusiveness, the century was disfigured by the most horrific inhumanities ever recorded. 'New humanism' arose in reaction, while the pace of interculturation outmoded racism and helped to stimulate the drive to make human rights coterminous with the concept of humankind. In the late 20th century, however, the problem of understanding the concept acquired two new dimensions which enriched its complexities and accentuated its agonies. First, social pressure to license abortion has created a new sub-human category: the unborn baby (formerly assumed to be fully human and to participate fully in human rights). In consequence, a new category called 'personhood' has now been invoked to justify the reclassification of the unborn, and the old question of how far humanhood is a biological or a cultural status has acquired a new focus of interest. Second, work in artficial intelligence and genetic engineering has made the human future as problematic as the human past. Do we face the 'post-human' future forecast by Francis Fukuyama? Or, given the unresolved history of the concept of humanity, can we simply yank at its elasticity and prolong the debate?

Political Philosophy **David Miller**

This book introduces readers to the concepts of political philosophy. David Miller starts by explaining why the subject is important and how it tackles basic ethical questions such as 'how should we live together in society?' The book looks at political authority, the reasons why we need politics at all, the limitations of politics, and whether there are areas of life that shouldn't be governed by politics. It explores the connections between political authority and justice, a constant theme in political philosophy, and the ways in which social justice can be used to regulate rather than destroy a market economy. David Miller discusses why nations are the natural units of government and whether the rise of multiculturalism and transnational co-operation will change this: will we ever see the formation of a world government?

Globalization **Manfred Steger**

'Globalization studies' is emerging as a new field that cuts across traditional disciplinary boundaries. This strong emphasis on interdisciplinarity requires students of globalization to familiarize themselves with literatures on subjects that have often been studied in isolation from each other. The greatest challenge facing today's globalization researcher lies, therefore, in connecting and synthesizing the various strands of knowledge in a way that does justice to the increasingly fluid and interdependent nature of our postmodern world. In short, globalization studies calls for an interdisciplinary approach broad enough to behold the 'big picture'. Such a comprehensive intellectual enterprise may well lead to the rehabilitation of the academic generalist whose status, for too long, has been overshadowed by the specialist.

The author argues that we should take comfort in the fact that the world is becoming a more interdependent place that enhances people's ability to recognize and acknowledge their common humanity.

Countries versus transnational corporations: A comparison

	Country	GDP ($ mil)	Corporation	Sales ($ mil)
1.	Denmark	174,363.0	General Motors	176,558.0
2.	Poland	154,146.0	Wal-Mart	166,809.0
3.	South Africa	131,127.0	Exxon Mobil	163,881.0
4.	Israel	99,068.0	Royal Dutch/Shell	105,366.0
5.	Ireland	84,861.0	IBM	87,548.0
6.	Malaysia	74,634.0	Siemens	75,337.0
7.	Chile	71,092.0	Hitachi	71,858.5
8.	Pakistan	59,880.0	Sony	60,052.7
9.	New Zealand	53,622.0	Honda Motor	54,773.5
10.	Hungary	48,355.0	Credit Suisse	49,362.0

SOURCE: Sales: *Fortune*, 31 July 2000. GDP: World Bank, *World Development Report 2000*.

American sociologist George Ritzer coined the term 'McDonaldization' to describe the wide-ranging sociocultural processes by which the principles of the fast-food restaurant are coming to dominate more and more sectors of American society, as well as the rest of the world. On the surface, these principles appear to be rational in their attempts to offer efficient and predictable ways of serving people's needs. However, looking behind the façade of repetitive TV commercials that claim to 'love to see you smile', we can identify a number of serious problems. For one, the generally low nutritional value of fast-food meals – and particularly their high fat content – has been implicated in the rise of serious health problems such as heart disease, diabetes, cancer, and juvenile obesity. Moreover, the impersonal, routine operations of 'rational' fast-service establishments actually undermine expressions of forms of cultural diversity. In the long run, the McDonaldization of the world amounts to the imposition of uniform standards that eclipse human creativity and dehumanize social relations.

Mathematics   **Timothy Gowers**

This is an attempt to convey the spirit of advanced mathematics
while making very few demands on the reader's prior knowledge
and technical competence. This is notoriously hard to do in a
subject that is full of complicated arguments and long calculations,
often couched in jargon that appears to be utterly impenetrable.

The book does not try to explain any jargon or present difficult
arguments and calculations in detail: even if this were desirable it
would be impossible to do satisfactorily in a short introduction.
Instead, it has the more modest aim of elucidating a few of the more
challenging *concepts* of mathematics, concepts such as infinity, the
square roots of negative numbers, curved space, and geometry in
four or more dimensions.

The way to understand these counterintuitive ideas is to begin with
much simpler ones. An important message of the book is that even a
concept as basic as that of a natural number (that is, one of the
numbers 1,2,3,4,5, . . . etc.) involves significant subtleties. Implicit
in our understanding of the natural numbers is an acceptance of
various arithmetical rules, which, after many years of schooling, we
come to use unquestioningly, to the point where we hardly notice
that we are doing so. Why, for example, is it easy to see that
$50\times 40 = 2000$? One possible justification is to say that
$$50\times 40 = (5\times 10)\times(4\times 10) = (5\times 4)\times (10\times 10) = 20\times 100 = 2000$$. This argument
may be convincing, but in the course of it we appeal to various
arithmetical principles, such as that $(ab)\times(cd)$ must equal
$(ac)\times(bd)$ for any four numbers a, b, c, and d.

Simple rules such as these are important for two reasons: they are
what we use to think about numbers in a general context, and they
help us define new sorts of numbers. To illustrate the first point,
suppose that I wish to prove the general fact that the square of any
odd number is odd. I will represent the number as $(2n + 1)$, do

the calculation $$(2n + 1)2 = 2n(2n + 1) + 2n + 1 = 4n2 + 2n + 2n + 1 = 4n2 + 4n + 1$$ and comment that since $4n2 + 4n$ is even, $4n2 + 4n + 1$ must be odd. But during the calculation I use rules for expanding brackets, I assume (implicitly) that $(4n2 + 4n) + 1$ is the same number as $4n2 + (4n + 1)$, and so on. Conversely, and more importantly, it turns out that just a few such rules are enough to do this calculation and many others like it.

The second point is more subtle, and is illustrated by the way the square root of minus one is introduced into mathematics. Since the square of any real number is positive, one could simply say that minus one does not have a square root. But instead, mathematicians take a symbol, i, and declare that it is (or represents) the square root of minus one. They then ask what else can be said about i other than that $i2 = -1$, and find that they can do calculations such as the following: $$(1 + i)2 = (1 + i) + i(1 + i) = 1 + i + i + i2 = 1 + 2i-1 = 2i.$$

What justifies such a calculation is not that it expresses a true fact about the pre-existing number i. Since i has been declared into existence, there is nothing to be discovered about it. Instead, we must decide for ourselves what principles to use when doing arithmetic that involves i. Fortunately, one principle stands out as by far the most natural and useful: that the simple arithmetical rules that are valid for real numbers should still be valid for numbers involving i. This guiding principle completely determines the answers to questions such as whether i has a square root, what $(2 + 3i)4$ is, and so on.

Notice that a very important reversal has taken place. The simple arithmetical rules are no longer facts that we observe about numbers we already understand. Instead, they take centre stage: when it comes to the new, unfamiliar numbers; all we know about them is that they obey the rules. The rules generate the numbers rather than the other way round.

This new perspective is of the utmost importance for mathematics in general. In the book, it is shown how other strange-seeming ideas lose much of their mystery when they are regarded as natural outgrowths of a few simple rules, rather than as pre-existing objects with properties waiting to be discovered. Even the rules themselves are usually natural generalizations of ones with which we are already familiar.

All of the book strives to be accessible to non-mathematicians, but the last chapter does so most obviously, as it is more about mathematicians than about mathematics. In this chapter, various commonly held views are held up to scrutiny. Examples are that the best mathematics is done by young people, that these people are almost always male, that most people dislike mathematics and have very little aptitude for it, that mathematicians make heavy use of computers, and that mathematics and music are intimately related.

> '... includes so much useful information and ideas it is quite incredible.'
>
> The Times

Logic **Graham Priest**

The cosmos is not a purely random mess. It shows very distinctive patterns: matter is structured into galaxies, which are structured, in turn, into stars and planetary systems, and on some of those planetary systems, matter is structured in such a way as to produce living creatures like you and me. What is the explanation for this? You might say that the explanation is provided by the laws of physics and biology. And so it may be. But why are the laws of physics and biology the way they are? After all, they could have been different. For example, gravity could have been a force of repulsion, not attraction. In that case, there would never have been stable chunks of matter, and life as we know it would have been impossible anywhere in the cosmos. Does this not give us excellent reason to believe in the existence of a creator of the cosmos: an intelligent being who brought into existence the cosmos, together with its physical and biological laws, for some purpose or other? In short, does not the fact that the physical cosmos is ordered in the way that it is give us reason to believe in the existence of a god of a certain kind?

You can choose to believe in the existence of God or you can choose not to. If God exists, all well and good. If not, then your belief is a minor inconvenience: it means that you will have wasted a bit of time in church, and maybe done a few things that you would not otherwise have wanted to do; but none of this is disastrous. Now suppose, on the other hand, that you choose not to believe in the existence of God. Again, either God exists or not. If God does not exist, all well and good. But if God *does* exist, boy are you in trouble! You are in for a lot of suffering in the afterlife; maybe for eternity if a bit of mercy isn't thrown in. So any wise person ought to believe in the existence of God. It's the only prudent course of action. This argument is now usually called *Pascal's Wager*, after the 17th-century philosopher Blaise Pascal, who first put it forward.

Logic and Hell

Let's suppose you take the wrong gamble on Pascal's Wager, and end up in Hell. After a few days, the Devil appears with an offer. God has commanded that you be shown some mercy. So the Devil has hatched a plan. He will give you one chance to get out of Hell. You can toss a coin; if it comes down heads, you are out and go to Heaven. If it comes down tails, you stay in Hell for ever. The coin is not a fair one, however, and the Devil has control of the odds. If you toss today, the chance of a head is $\frac{1}{2}$ (i.e. $1-1/2$). If you wait until tomorrow, the chances go up to $\frac{3}{4}$ (i.e. $1-1/2^2$). You sum up the information:

	Escape stay in Hell
Toss today (d)	$0.5\backslash + 10^6\ 0.5\backslash -10^6$
Toss tomorrow (m)	$0.75\backslash + 10^6\ 0.25\backslash -10^6$

17. Tweedledum and Tweedledee.

Escaping has a very large positive value; staying in Hell has a very large negative value. Moreover, these values are the same today as tomorrow. It is true that if you wait until tomorrow, you might have to spend an extra day in Hell, but one day is negligible compared with the infinite number of days that are to follow. Doing the calculations confirms this reasoning, so you decide to wait until tomorrow.

But tomorrow the Devil comes to you and says that if you wait one more day, the odds will get even better: they will go up to 7/8. After doing the calculations, you get much the same result as you did the previous day, and decide to wait until the next day. The trouble is that *every* day the Devil comes to you and offers you better odds if you wait until the next day. The odds get better, day by day, as follows:

$$1-1/2, 1-1/2^2, 1-1/2^3, 1-1/2^4, \ldots, 1-1/2^n, \ldots$$

Hence, every day you do the rational thing and wait until the next day. The result is that you never toss the coin at all, so you stay in Hell for ever! Tossing on *any* day has to be better than that. So it looks as though the only rational thing to do is to be irrational!

> '. . . *a splendid fist of warming up logic for the general palate.*'
> The Guardian

Cryptography   **Fred Piper and Sean Murphy**

In this fascinating introduction to how cryptography actually works, the authors highlight its all-pervasive impact on modern society. In doing so, they demystify the art of cryptography, highlighting the difficulties and ever-increasing importance of data protection and authentication in the modern world.

Cryptography has been a significant historical influence for more than 2,000 years. Traditionally its main users were governments and the military. Prior to the 1970s, cryptography was a 'black art', understood and practised by only a few government and military personnel. It is now a well-established academic discipline that is taught in many universities.

> *'A perfect pocket primer for anyone interested in Cryptography.'*
> Simon Singh

Quantum Theory   John Polkinghorne

It is no exaggeration to regard the discovery (in the mid-1920s) of quantum theory as being one of the most outstanding intellectual achievements of the 20th century and as constituting a real revolution in our understanding of the physical world since the days of Isaac Newton. What had been considered to be the arena of clear and determinate process was found to be, at its subatomic roots, cloudy and fitful in its behaviour. Compared with this revolutionary change, the great discoveries of special and general relativity seem not much more than interesting variations on classical themes. Indeed, Albert Einstein, who had been the progenitor of relativity theory, found modern quantum mechanics so little to his metaphysical taste that he remained implacably opposed to it right to the end of his life.

If the study of quantum physics teaches one anything, it is that the world is full of surprises. No one would have supposed beforehand that there could be entities that sometimes behaved as if they were waves and sometimes behaved as if they were particles. This realization was forced upon the physics community by the intransigent necessity of actual empirical experience. As Bohr once said, the world is not only stranger than we thought; it is stranger than we could think. Even logic has to be modified when it is applied to the quantum world.

> *'John Polkinghorne has brought to life that most mysterious and perplexing of revolutions in understanding and has made its mysteries accessible.'*
>
> Peter Atkins

The End of the World   **Bill McGuire**

We live in a comfy, cosseted world that would be alien and unrecognizable to the majority of the earth's deprived and struggling inhabitants, whose lives are a constant battle against the elements. It is a world that is coming to an end, perhaps due to events beyond our control, but most likely through our inability to work with nature rather than against it. In the opening year of the new millennium, 1 in 30 people on the planet was affected by natural disasters. How much time do we have before we all succumb to flood, storm, and quake, or to the rare but globally devastating super-eruptions, mega-tsunami, and impacts from space?

The End of the World enforces the idea that our global, technological society has developed only by Nature's consent, during a period of relative geological and climatic calm that cannot endure. Just 600 generations of our race have lived since the glaciers of the last ice age retreated to their polar fastnesses, but already we face the prospect of dramatic and potentially devastating climate change. Global warming arising from industrialization is real, and its impact is already becoming apparent through rapidly rising temperatures and greater incidences of extreme weather. Notwithstanding half-hearted attempts to reduce greenhouse gas emissions, temperatures may rise by up to 8 degrees Celsius by the end of the century, with sea levels up to almost 90 cm higher. Water wars, famines of Biblical proportions, and mass migrations will make our current world seem a haven of peace and stability, and will threaten to unravel the fabric of our global economic and social framework. Floods and storms will batter the vulnerable in the developing world, but will take an increasing toll in the affluent countries too. Even if we conquer our stupidity and seriously tackle global warming now, temperatures will continue to rise for centuries and sea levels for millennia. If we do, ultimately, manage to save ourselves from the fire, it may only be to face incarceration in the fridge, for, despite our involuntary attempts to stave it off, the great ice sheets are merely biding their time, and will return once again to sweep across the continents of the northern hemisphere. Perhaps we can adapt, albeit with great difficulty, to a hothouse earth, but can we survive a world where ice a mile thick buries much of Europe and North America?

Global warming is with us now and we know that within several thousand years the ice is due to return, but other threats to our comfortable existence are less predictable. *The End of the World* also takes a close look at the latest research findings to elucidate the threats posed by the enormous geological forces building beneath our planet's surface. A collapsing volcano in the Canary Islands threatens to crash into the North Atlantic, generating giant sea waves capable of swamping the great cities of the eastern United States. Somewhere in Southeast Asia or around the Pacific Rim, a giant volcanic blast capable of blacking out the sun for years and leading to global freezing and starvation is well overdue. More imminently, a huge quake is forecast to strike Tokyo in the next few decades, causing destruction totalling 7 trillion US\$ and triggering global economic meltdown. The book also casts its net wider to encompass the menace from space and assess the true threat from impacting asteroids and comets. About a thousand chunks of rock a kilometre or more wide cross the earth's orbit, about a third of which we have spotted. Of the remainder, one could strike tomorrow, plunging the world into

18. A possible end to the world? An atomic explosion.

'cosmic winter' and straining to the limit our society's capacity to survive.

This book presents an essentially personal perspective from the author on the future of our society and our race. His viewpoint can hardly be described as optimistic, but is not intended to be so. Rather, the book should be considered a wake-up call. So far we have been lucky, but good fortune cannot last forever. Short of a so-called 'extinction-level event', such as the huge comet impact that ended the dinosaurs' long reign, it is unlikely that any other foreseeable natural event will be capable of wiping out all 6 billion of us. It is equally unlikely, however, that our race and our modern society will continue to thrive without being knocked back, perhaps more than once, by a global natural catastrophe so large that there will be nowhere to run to and nowhere to hide.

Forthcoming
Chaos, Leonard Smith
Humankind, Felipe Fernandez-Armesto
International Relations, Paul Wilkinson

Visit the
VERY SHORT
INTRODUCTIONS
Web site

www.oup.co.uk/vsi

➤ **Information** about all published titles

➤ News of **forthcoming books**

➤ **Extracts** from the books, including titles
not yet published

➤ **Reviews** and views

➤ **Links** to other **web sites** and main
OUP web page

➤ Information about **VSIs in translation**

➤ **Contact** the editors

➤ **Order** other **VSIs** on-line

Expand your collection of
VERY SHORT INTRODUCTIONS